The same as you?

A review of services for people with learning disabilities

Ministerial foreword

It is over 20 years since the last policy initiative on learning disability services in Scotland. Although there has been progress in many areas since then, it has not been consistent. Overall, the pattern of services in Scotland is not as advanced as in many countries in Europe. So, I very much welcome this wide-ranging review, and the way it has been carried out. In it we meet the commitment in our Programme for Government 'Making It Work Together' to publish in 2000 our proposals for services for people with learning disabilities.

The Learning Disability Review has succeeded in involving many of those with an interest, especially those who use services and their carers, at different points in the journey. I know from meeting people how much that has been welcomed and valued. I was involved in the review-visiting projects, at one of the seminars and answering questions in a live internet session. I was very impressed by the desire for change, the reasonableness and responsibility of those pressing for it and the willingness of agencies to respond.

This review began by looking at services, especially in social and healthcare, and their relationship with education, housing, employment and other areas. However, its focus changed to include people's lifestyles. That is what matters. Services are there to support people in their daily lives.

We are committed to improving the quality of life for people with disabilities. The review reflects our wider policies including **social inclusion**, equality and fairness, and the opportunity for people to improve themselves through continuous learning. These are just as important and just as relevant to people with learning disabilities as they are to all of us.

The focus of the report is consistent with our existing policies on community care. 'Modernising Community Care' wants better results for people through quicker and better decision-making, greater emphasis on care at home and agencies working more closely together. Our desire to improve the general health of people with learning disabilities is also directly related to our aims in 'Towards a Healthier Scotland'. The responsibility of the Joint Future Group, which I chair, is to build on both these documents and identify and promote good practice in working with others.

People with learning disabilities should be able to lead normal lives. We want them to:

- be included, better understood and supported by the communities in which they live;

- have information about their needs and the services available, so that they can take part, more fully, in decisions about them;

- be at the centre of decision-making and have more control over their care;

- have the same opportunities as others to get a job, develop as individuals, spend time with family and friends, enjoy life and get the extra support they need to do this; and

- be able to use local services wherever possible and special services if they need them.

People with learning disabilities want to make a positive contribution to society. Communities and individuals must learn to recognise their needs and respond more positively to them. A programme to improve public awareness is part of helping them to have a better quality of life.

I particularly welcome the opportunities for people to have more say and more control over their lives. Professionals need to acknowledge their limits and the rights of others. Using **direct payments**, **brokerage** and advocacy services more will help people have more influence.

Lastly, the review recommends that for all but a few people, health and social care should be provided in their own homes or in community settings alongside the rest of the population. I know that many people will welcome this idea. However, we must put in place the appropriate services and support to allow people to live properly in the community, to allow the rest of the long-stay institutions to close.

In welcoming the vision for the future, we have to be realistic and recognise the many pressures there are for resources both nationally and locally. We want and need to make the lives of people with learning disabilities better. Over time that will need more resources but now we can make better use of the considerable funds that are available in all sectors. The review gives agencies very clear signals about the level of change needed. People with learning disabilities and their carers must see early evidence of that beginning to take shape.

Iain Gray MSP

Deputy Minister for Community Care

How the review was done

1   We formed four main groups (see appendix 7 for details):

- an interdepartmental steering group;
- a multidisciplinary working group;
- a users' and carers' group; and
- a stakeholders' group made up of experts in the field.

2   We set up six smaller task groups with specific responsibilities to discuss **complex needs**, best practice, training, the **mapping of services**, best-value, and children's services.

3   We carried out a major consultation to get a good understanding of:

- learning disabilities;
- the experiences people have of services;
- the demand for services; and
- what the solutions to service shortfalls might be.

4   We used a range of methods including the following.

Written views

We wrote to over 600 people and agencies inviting their views on current services and on the shape of future services.

Website (http://www.scotland.gov.uk/ldsr/)

We set up an interactive website to give and receive information about the review and to generate on-going debate. Iain Gray, Deputy Minister for Community Care, held a live session on the web to hear the concerns and hopes people have. The website contains most of the material we used.

User and carer roadshows

The user and carer group held 11 roadshows across Scotland to get a national view on what people with learning disabilities and their carers need and want.

Site visits

We visited sites across Scotland to see, at first hand, good and new, creative projects.

Meetings

We met people who used services, carers, staff and representatives from professional organisations to listen to what they felt was important now and in the future.

Conferences

We held four national conferences across the country:

- explaining the reason for and scope of the review;
- examining the best use of resources;
- discussing good practice; and
- looking at the shape of future services.

Workshops

We held four smaller workshops on:

- children's issues;
- people with **complex needs**;
- staff development; and
- a brainstorming day for all the groups involved in the review.

Research, surveys and analysis

We carried out the following research and surveys.

- A survey of people with learning disabilities and their families about social and healthcare services.
- A survey of housing solutions and a review of international literature on housing options for those with learning disabilities.
- Research on the general health needs of people with learning disabilities.

- Research on the needs of people with **profound** and **multiple disabilities**.
- Research on the needs of those with **challenging behaviour**.
- An analysis of those with learning disabilities who are held under the Mental Health (Scotland) Act 1984.
- A policy paper on public education about people with learning disabilities.
- Analysis of community care plans, health improvement plans, trust implementation plans, children's plans, Scottish Health Advisory Service reports, and relevant Social Work Services Inspectorate reports.

Adults and children

5   Our evidence and recommendations relate to services for both adults and children unless we say they are for a particular group such as older people or adolescents. Where we make recommendations relating to local authority services these should be considered by those dealing with adults *and* those dealing with children.

Contents

1 Understanding the issues

"Disabled people, whatever the origin, nature and seriousness of their handicaps and disabilities, have the same fundamental rights as their fellow citizens of the same age, which implies first and foremost the right to enjoy a decent life, as normal and full as possible."

United Nations (1975) The Declaration on the Rights of Disabled Persons

1   People with learning disabilities have always been part of society. Sometimes they have been treated well, and sometimes they have been treated in ways that are unacceptable. Sometimes what seemed the best approach has, looking back, appeared lacking in understanding. More disturbingly there have been some well-documented serious instances of abuse. Always it has been a matter of how people deal with one another. There are important issues of human rights, responsibilities and **social inclusion** that we all need to look at if progress is to be made.

2   People with learning disabilities and their families are entitled to as full a life as possible. They are entitled to feel valued and to be included in society. They and their carers generally know best what support they need and they should be at the heart of decisions that affect their lives. Barriers that prevent people getting the right help quickly need to be removed and support services should be improved. We all need a better understanding of people with learning disabilities if they and their carers are to get better services and opportunities.

3   People with learning disabilities need help from a number of different agencies and professionals at different stages in their lives. Generally, people with learning disabilities want, and should be able, to use the local services that everybody else uses. These services need to adapt their approaches to meet the needs of people with learning disabilities. If local services cannot meet particular needs, specialist services should add to, not replace, ordinary services.

Who are people with learning disabilities?

4   There is a range of views about how useful definitions are, and how they apply in different settings. However, it is important to have a definition

so that people with learning disabilities get the services and support they need, and so that agencies can plan these services better. Our definition includes traditional descriptions from medicine and education along with details of the support that people need to be able to do the things they would like. We provide a more detailed discussion of definitions in Appendix 3. In the next few years the causes of learning disability are likely to be understood much better. The effects on our social, health and educational services will stay the same.

Our definition

5　People with learning disabilities have a significant, lifelong condition that started before adulthood, that affected their development and which means they need help to:

- understand information;
- learn skills; and
- cope independently.

6　People with learning disabilities should have a range of support and services to meet the following needs.

- Everyday needs

For example, a place to live, security, social and personal relationships, leisure, recreation and work opportunities.

- Extra needs because of their learning disability

For example, help to understand information, support to make decisions and plan, learn skills, help with communication, **mobility** or personal care.

- Complex needs

For example, needs arising from both learning disability and from other difficulties such as physical and **sensory impairment**, mental health problems or behavioural difficulties.

7   For any of these needs the level of support will vary. A person with learning disabilities may need:

- occasional or short-term support;
- limited support, for example, only during periods of change or crisis;
- regular long-term support, perhaps every day; or
- constant and highly intensive support if they have complex or other needs which are related.

As one person told us:

"You need to take time to get to know us – we are all different."

8   So people with learning disabilities have a range of needs which will change during their lifetime. Professionals need to help people plan for the future. For many people with learning disabilities, particularly those with **complex needs**, organisations need to work together with the individual and their family to plan and support them.

People with learning disabilities should have the following.

- Services that promote and protect their health and welfare, help them lead lives which are as normal as possible and are best suited to their needs, whether at home, in schools, health services or other settings.
- Information, advice and help to get education, work and leisure that offers personal fulfilment, consistency and security, best meets their needs and personal preferences, and helps them to be included and accepted within local communities.
- Ordinary homes which are private, secure, comfortable and safe.

People with learning disabilities and their families should:

- have accurate and easily accessible information at the right time about what services and support are available locally and nationally, in a number of different ways;
- be involved when professionals make decisions about what help to

provide, so that they can have a real choice about what happens to them; and

- get independent advice and advocacy services when they need them.

Families and carers should have:

- a range of help to support them including training and advice to look after a person with a learning disability;
- access to professionals who take into account and find ways to meet their needs as carers (whether they are parents, brothers and sisters or other family members); and
- access to short breaks.

Communities need to:

- have greater understanding of people with learning disabilities and how they can contribute to the community; and
- be involved in supporting people with learning disabilities and their families to achieve their rights.

Employers need to:

- overcome prejudice associated with employing people with learning disabilities, and play their part in helping them to reach their potential.

How many people in Scotland have a learning disability?

9   We do not have enough detailed information about the number of people in Scotland who have learning disabilities. While there are some reported differences across the UK, studies suggest that, in Scotland:

- 20 people for every 1,000 have a mild or moderate learning disability; and
- 3 to 4 people for every 1,000 have a **profound** or **multiple disability**[1].

10   On this basis, there are around 120,000 people in Scotland with learning disabilities. Using information from three local areas which appears to be reasonably thorough we estimate that only 30,000 people are in regular contact with local authorities or the health service in Scotland. Others may have occasional or short-term contacts.

11   Research suggests that 15-20,000 people need a lot of help to cope with daily living[2]. Of these about 25% (4,000 to 5,000) are children and young people aged under 16. A further 25% (4,000 to 5,000) have **complex needs** which need a lot of support. People with learning disabilities are often not as healthy as the rest of the population. They may need more health support than primary care alone can provide[3]. As people's learning disability becomes more severe, so does the likelihood of complex health needs such as epilepsy, **mobility** and **sensory impairment**. People with learning disabilities may need support and services because of mental health problems[4]. Around 30% to 42% of children with learning disabilities may need help for emotional and behavioural problems[5]. Older people with learning disabilities have more mental health problems. This is particularly so for people with Down's syndrome who may get **early onset dementia**[6].

12   The number of people with learning disabilities in the UK has increased over the last 35 years. Researchers estimate an increase of 1.2% a year between 1960 and 1995 of people with severe learning disabilities, with a significant increase in those who are older[7].

13   This means that since 1965 the number of people with severe learning disabilities has increased by 50%. The number of people with moderate needs has probably increased in much the same way.

14   In 1965, many people with severe disabilities were cared for in hospitals, though the then increasing number in hospital in Scotland (about 7,000) included many people with mild disabilities and some who had no disability[8]. By 1998 less than 2,450 people with learning disabilities were cared for in hospitals[9]. The rest, including 90% of those with **complex needs**, were cared for in the community. These are very significant changes affecting:

- people with learning disabilities;
- their families;

- staff working in local authorities and health settings; and
- society in general.

15   Research suggests that the number of people with learning disabilities will continue to grow by over 1% a year over the next 10 years[10]. And, more will live longer, so the needs of people with learning disabilities will change.

Who provides support?

Families

16   By far the most support is provided by parents, brothers and sisters and other relatives. This is a lifelong commitment and it is striking that family carers are often given the responsibility for (and expected to provide) social and nursing care that many professional agencies refuse to offer. Research suggests that:

- 25% of people with learning disabilities have a carer aged 65 or over;
- 20% have two carers aged 70 or over; and
- 11% have only one aged 70 or over[11].

Younger and older carers tend to have different expectations. Younger carers may be looking at how best their child can develop, whereas older carers are likely to be worried about how their child will be looked after when they die.

Local authority and health services

17   Local authority and health services include:

- community care services;
- child care services;
- criminal justice services;
- primary care health services provided by doctors, health visitors and district nurses;
- pharmaceutical services;
- dental services;
- ophthalmic services;
- pre-school and school education;

- housing;
- leisure and transport services.

Experiences differ a lot from person to person and area to area. The relationship a person has with primary care services is very important. In some areas people with learning disabilities enjoy the same services in the same way as the rest of the population. In others, professionals do not understand people's needs properly. It is all too common for people to miss out on, or be inappropriately referred to and accepted by, specialist services. We need local authority and health services to work together better to help people find their way through the system.

Voluntary organisations

18   For many years, voluntary organisations have provided a wide range of very important services and support for adults and children with learning disabilities and their families. The residential and other services they provide are often excellent, partly because of the length of their experience, but mainly because they focus on personal relationships. They are also highly-valued for being realistic and coming up with new ideas, as sources of accurate and accessible information, and for providing effective advocacy.

Specialist health and local authority services

19   Specialist health services in hospital and community settings have been focused more and more on those people with learning disabilities who have **complex needs**. Community Learning Disability Teams (CLDTs) have developed in most areas in Scotland over the last 20 years. Some are made up of nurses and psychologists, while others have social workers attached to them. Some provide services to adults, while others provide for children as well. Their links to other agencies also vary. Local authority specialist services have increased to meet the needs of the greater number of people with learning disabilities in the community. While CLDTs have provided a valuable service in many parts of the country, we need more consistent structures that make sure they are co-ordinated and reduce the chance of duplication.

Where does the money go?

20   Local authorities and health boards spend about £275 million a year on services specifically for people with learning disabilities.   About

£115 million[12] is on health services, and £160 million[13] on social care services. Between 1980 and 1998 the number of people with learning disabilities in hospital in Scotland has fallen by nearly two-thirds from 6,500 to less than 2,450[14]. At the same time the number of residents in care homes for people with learning disabilities has increased from 1,000[15] to 4,800[16] with another 600 people living in supported accommodation. We also know of about 900 mostly older people in other homes who have some degree of learning disability. This is a significant shift, although the pace of change in Scotland has been slower than in other parts of the UK and much of Europe.

21   We can see this by comparing how resources are spent in Scotland with England and Wales. In England, health and local authorities spend £59[17, 18] each year on learning disability services for every person in the population. In Wales the figure is £63[19]. In Scotland, the equivalent is only £54[20, 21]. In part this is to do with the priority given to learning disability services in England and Wales over the last 20 years. In Scotland 37% of the spend goes on hospitals, while in England only 15% is tied up in hospitals. Figure 1 below makes this clear.

Figure 1: Where the money goes England, Scotland and Wales compared

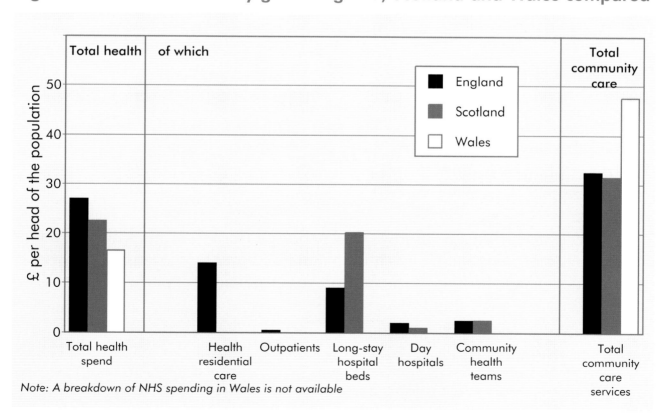

Note: A breakdown of NHS spending in Wales is not available

In Wales 74% of total spending goes through local authority community care services, while in Scotland only 58% does. The result is that as well as having the lowest total spend on services for people with learning disabilities, Scotland has even less well resourced community services for people with learning disabilities, their families and carers.

22   Levels and style of service also vary a lot within Scotland. The highest-spending local authority spends seven times as much as the lowest for every person of the total population[22]. There are also differences in the amount health boards spend; the highest and lowest differ by 37% for every person[23]. (This figure does not include the islands.) During the review, people who used services and their carers said that how well they were treated often seemed to depend on where they lived or, indeed, on the different professionals they were working with.

23   Carers said that help was often only provided when there was a crisis (when it was most expensive). They said a little support earlier might have made their lives easier and cost less.

24   Families receive very different levels and quality of service in nearby authorities or even in different areas of the same social work or health authority. The reasons behind many decisions are not clear.

Putting people first

25   Many professionals and managers agree that things need to change to help people with learning disabilities have fuller lives. But change is not easy. Many of the ways local authorities and health services organise accommodation and support for people with learning disabilities tend towards keeping things the same.

26   The review offers an opportunity to change from thinking which is led by services to thinking which is led by people's needs; from people with learning disabilities having to depend on separate care services, to their being able to use everyday services more.

Seven principles

27   We consulted widely during the course of the review on a number of principles which we thought were central to helping people with learning

disabilities lead full and active lives. Seven principles emerged and we have taken account of these in all our considerations and recommendations.

- People with learning disabilities should be valued. They should be asked and encouraged to contribute to the community they live in. They should not be picked on or treated differently from others.
- People with learning disabilities are individual people.
- People with learning disabilities should be asked about the services they need and be involved in making choices about what they want.
- People with learning disabilities should be helped and supported to do everything they are able to.
- People with learning disabilities should be able to use the same local services as everyone else, wherever possible.
- People with learning disabilities should benefit from specialist social, health and educational services.
- People with learning disabilities should have services which take account of their age, abilities and other needs.

2 The way ahead

1   Local authorities and health boards have made progress on joint planning across boundaries since the Community Care Act was introduced[24]. Local authorities have lead responsibility for planning community care and for producing children's services plans. More users and carers have been involved in planning community care. 'Modernising Community Care'[25] promotes and strengthens joint planning and joint working at a local level. But strategies and plans have no value in themselves. Better information, communication and effective collaboration are essential to achieve our medium and longer-term aims.

2   Chapters 3 and 6 look at the need for better information, communication and working together. Chapters 4 and 5 aim to change dramatically where people stay and how they spend their days. In this chapter we recommend another seven important developments to improve the future for people with learning disabilities.

- Firstly, we need a clear focus within local authority and health planning systems on agencies working together to develop services for people with learning disabilities. This will include a requirement for them to produce 'partnership in practice' agreements. Local authorities should take responsibility for all non-health-related needs of people with learning disabilities, their families and carers. Health boards must make sure they provide an effective health service for people with learning disabilities.
- Secondly, we need to set up local area co-ordinators to improve local services.
- Thirdly, we need longer-term planning to support people with learning disabilities, and 'personal life plans' for those people with learning disabilities who want them.
- Fourthly, we need a 'change fund' to help local authorities move quickly from the present position towards our vision for people with learning disabilities.
- Fifthly, we need to strengthen people's entitlement to **direct payments**.
- Sixthly, we need to set up a Scottish centre for learning disability.
- Finally, we need to develop a Scottish service network for **autistic spectrum disorders**.

Partnership in practice

3   To make sure this happens consistently throughout Scotland we propose that local authorities, health boards and primary care trusts should prepare 'partnership in practice' (PIP) agreements for learning disability services in their areas. The Scottish Executive should see the first agreements by 1 June 2001 and these should cover services for children and adults for a three-year period. These agreements should form part of, and not be on top of, the community care, children's and health planning processes (such as health improvement plans (HIPs), trust implementation plans (TIPs), local health care co-operative plans and individual practice plans). The PIP should draw together the information that is already in existing plans to make sure all the agencies involved in planning services for adults and children with learning disabilities can come to an agreement. Part of a local PIP should be a section for promoting health linked to local and national health promotion strategies.

4   Though the areas in Scotland to be covered by each PIP should be agreed locally, we recommend that generally a PIP is developed for each local authority area or group of local authorities working together. We expect the important contribution currently made by the voluntary sector in providing services to be a central consideration and we expect these agreements to be developed by consulting users and carers. We set out a number of the main elements which should be included in the next few pages.

Assessing needs and planning

5   The agreement should include needs assessment covering children and adults with learning disabilities. The agreement should look specifically at:

- support for families and carers;
- physical disabilities and **sensory impairment**;
- mental health;
- **profound** and **multiple disability;**
- **challenging behaviour**;
- offending behaviour;
- **autistic spectrum disorders**;
- ethnic-minority issues;
- children who are changing schools;
- young people who plan to leave school and will need adult services;

- ageing; and
- the needs of people with 'life-limiting conditions' and those with **palliative care** needs.

6   The agreement should outline the plans for developing and **commissioning** accommodation and social support in line with our recommendations in this review. It should map current services and include a plan for providing accommodation in the community and support for people with learning disabilities living with their families, and for their families. The first PIP agreement should include plans for setting up and maintaining a local register of adults and children with learning disabilities. We expect registers to contain details of people who:

- currently receive services;
- have been assessed;and
- may need services in the future and want to be on the register.

7   We need to have a range of services in place to meet the needs of people with learning disabilities, especially those with **complex needs**. In particular, health boards, trusts and local authorities should make sure that:

- adults and children with learning disabilities have access to the full range of general health and social services;
- adults and children with learning disabilities can benefit from specialist health and social care services, including hospital and residential services, when this is in their best interests;
- appropriate support, training and education is provided to staff working in primary care and other general health and social care settings; and
- services for people with learning disabilities are co-ordinated locally including those with **complex needs**.

8   Health boards should have health promotion strategies which look at the needs of people with learning disabilities and their families. Positive health includes many of the ideas in this review – fulfilling potential, good relationships, support for families and carers and so on.

9   Local psychiatric services and learning disability services should agree

arrangements for working with, providing advice to, and referring clients *between* services. In particular this should focus on the needs of people:

- with mild learning disabilities;
- with a **dual diagnosis**;
- who are experiencing problems in adolescence or old age; and
- who have dementia at an early age.

10   Health boards and trusts still have important responsibilities for people with learning disabilities and their families. They must make sure they provide as full a health service for people with learning disabilities as for anyone else. They should provide a small number of both assessment and treatment places for people with **complex needs** and for people who are **detained** in hospitals. There should be agreed ways of working with local authority social work departments and primary care colleagues on placing people in and releasing them from hospitals.

11   The agreement should include **advocacy** and other measures which place people who use services and carers at the centre of the decision-making process.

12   Local authorities should have the main responsibility for all non health related needs of people with learning disabilities and their families. This includes providing accommodation, education, social care and support, day services, employment, leisure and recreation, transport, information and communication.

13   Local authorities have always had responsibility in this field under their social work role. Many are now developing the broader approaches described above which help promote **social inclusion**. For long-stay patients who have left hospital, as for others, accommodation and social support should be the responsibility of local authorities.

14   Many people with learning disabilities have conditions which specialists are very familiar with, but these are all too often neglected if there is no specialist involved. To neglect special health needs is as much a failure to put services at the centre of people's lives as to neglect the need for friendships.

15   Local authority and health boards must make sure all professionals work together, whatever agency they work in and that in future they use specialist medical, nursing, paramedical and social care professional skills to the best advantage.

Human resource strategies

16   Local authorities and health boards will need to put human resource strategies into place so plans can be put into practice effectively. Many of the developments we outline here or later, such as clarifying responsibilities, appointing local area co-ordinators and plans for closing long-stay hospitals will all affect staff. The changes which will need to be carried out as a result of this review can only be put in place properly if local authorities and health boards look at the significant training and retraining needs of front-line staff. Nurses currently working in long-stay hospitals are one priority group; support and residential care workers are another.

17   The 'partnership in practice' agreement should include a human resource strategy which builds on the principles of lifelong learning as set out in 'Learning Together – Lifelong Learning Strategy of the NHS in Scotland'. This says that staff can expect support from their employer in helping them keep up to date and get more skilled.

18   The 'partnership in practice' agreement should include an outline of:

- the human resource issues involved;
- whether any of the plans mean that the principles of **TUPE** should be used; and
- how the agencies involved plan to work together to put an effective strategy in place.

Recommendation 1   Each local authority or group of authorities and health boards should draw up a 'partnership in practice' agreement by 1 June 2001.

Co-ordinating local areas

19   We looked at the way services were developing in other countries and were particularly interested in an idea from Western Australia. This looked at

supporting people to live in their own communities. Local area co-ordination in Western Australia is an approach driven by the needs of people and is designed around each person. Local area co-ordinators provide funding directly to the customer to buy what they need, rather than using services from an agency paid for using a block grant.

20   In chapter 3 we refer to the difficulties people with learning disabilities and their carers have in getting information about what services are available. Many people also said that professionals displayed a lack of knowledge about learning disabilities. We believe that a specialist worker dedicated to working with a small number of people using services in one area would help people and their families through the current maze of systems.

21   Local area co-ordinators could have a number of different professional backgrounds. Each local area co-ordinator will support about 50 people so that they know them personally and can respond to individual needs. The precise number of people to be supported will be for local areas to decide. The co-ordinator's role is on many levels (individual, family, agency, community), and includes many areas (housing, including supported accommodation, employment, health, education, respite and so on). They will co-ordinate services and provide information, family support and funding to individuals and their families. We think the local area co-ordinators may be best placed within local health care co-operatives. In some areas they may need to work with more than one co-operative.

22   The local area co-ordinators' main task will be to make sure that other services are available which meet people's needs. They will:

- help people who use services decide what their needs are, and make plans for the future;
- with a budget, provide funding directly to people who use services, and try to get hold of new funding where there are gaps in services;
- provide information and help people get advocacy services;
- build relationships with people with disabilities and their families;
- support individuals and families to develop and maintain strong networks;
- help people who use services to co-ordinate the way support and services are provided;

- work with other individuals and agencies to encourage people with disabilities to be included in society (for example, with the key workers to be set up by the Beattie Committee[26]);
- make connections with members, groups and agencies from local communities;
- set joint aims for themselves, users and carers and monitor the quality and quantity of services provided to people with learning disabilities; and
- deal with complaints and any conflicts between people using services and their carers, families and professionals.

23   The co-ordinators will be responsible to a joint management committee made up of local authority, health and voluntary sector representatives as well as local users and carers. They will send regular reports to their joint management committee, who will also help to sort out any complaints. The exact nature of the responsibilities of local co-ordinators will be decided by the joint management committees of the areas they serve.

24   Local area co-ordinators have an important role in carrying out assessments and overseeing how learning disability services are co-ordinated.

25   Helping people with learning disabilities to lead full lives means better assessment of their social and healthcare needs. This should include what a person wants, what strengths, skills, problems and needs the person has, and what they need to realise their goals.

Recommendation 2   Health boards and local authorities should agree to appoint local area co-ordinators for learning disabilities from current resources used for managing care and co-ordinating services. Initial training for putting local area co-ordinators in place will begin in Autumn 2001.

A personal life plan

26   This section identifies the need for better longer-term planning for people with learning disabilities across the many services and types of support available. Any assessments for community care, health or children's services must have clear outcomes. From the point of the Future Needs Assessment

onwards and for all adults, we suggest that this takes the form of a new 'personal life plan'. This plan would be for everyone who has a learning disability and wants a life plan. The plan should describe how the person, his or her family and professionals, will work together to help that person lead a fuller life. **Brokerage services** should be part of what is offered. This is where the person with a learning disability has someone to act as a go-between for them to get what is needed. These have led to more person-centred outcomes especially for people who have not managed to get settled by using more traditional services. They can be a cost-effective way to break away from traditional methods.

27   The local area co-ordinator will be responsible for making sure that each person who wants to, has the opportunity to develop a life plan. The co-ordinator should write down the life plan and each person, their carer and their **advocate** or representative should have a copy. This plan will replace the existing community care assessment. Co-ordinators should:

- find out whether other people are visiting the person, what they are doing and whether they can use the same information to do an assessment together;
- tell the person that they are carrying out an assessment, what they will do and how long it will take;
- take account of language needs and cultural practices;
- tell the person what kinds of decisions depend on the assessment and what might happen; and
- at the end of an assessment, tell the person, and their family or carers if appropriate, what happens next.

28   The life plan will include healthcare needs including dental, ophthalmic, pharmaceutical, hearing, communication and physiotherapy needs as well as any other special support. It will set out the person's assessed care needs including:

- short breaks for the person or their carer;
- meaningful work or other opportunities during the day;
- further education;
- housing and transport needs; and
- how each of these should be met.

29   Plans for children drawn up at the time of Future Needs Assessment must link to any other assessment or **Record of Needs**. There will be a regular review of the life plan so that the family can get more involved. Everyone who signs up for the plan will be able to ask for a review whenever it seems necessary. We suggest a yearly detailed review of the life plan for people with more **complex needs** living at home, and those in long-stay hospitals. This will allow the co-ordinator to plan future care in a non-hospital based environment.

30   Above all it is important that a person with a learning disability, their family or carer should not only feel involved in, but also own the plan. The plan will focus on the person. It will spell out their wishes and preferences. The plan must concentrate on how to build on their strengths, to develop them as individuals and to help them lead active and fulfilling lives. Wherever possible plans should spell out how the person with a learning disability can actively contribute to the community. It should look at what is in the best interests of the person with a learning disability in a very thorough way focusing on needs and what is available.

Recommendation 3   **Everyone with a learning disability who wants to, should be able to have a 'personal life plan'. (Recommendation 26 builds on this.)**

A change fund

31   We recognise that local authorities can do much more to improve care and support for people with learning disabilities, including where people stay and how they spend their days. They can only partly achieve this by using existing resources more effectively and they will need more money.

32   Hospitals, care homes and day care serve about 17,000 people, 2,450[27] in hospitals and 14,300[28] in social care. So, the scale of change is huge. We believe agencies will need financial help to manage this change.

33   **Bridging finance** is one of the methods that has been used to bring about change in the NHS. It has provided over £150 million of help towards the cost of setting up new services while running down the old ones. There are no similar facilities to support change in social care services at the moment.

34   We believe people who use services and their carers will welcome the new directions proposed but may have concerns about how the changes will affect them in the short term. Experience suggests that people who use existing services will worry about change in case they lose essential support without anything being put in its place. They may need time to see for themselves the benefits of a new and very different set of services. Changing the patterns of care will mean taking these anxieties into account.

35   Local authorities, for their own services and those they commission from (mostly) the voluntary sector, will not be able to manage and pay for old and new services at the same time. They will need help with the costs of creating new services while keeping the old ones going until it is appropriate to close them down. Funding is also needed to re-direct existing services, develop new ones and to pay for training to improve the skills of staff.

36   Alongside that we have recognised the need to invest in certain important areas such as short-term breaks or **advocacy** if people with learning disabilities are to be properly supported in the community. We see a national 'change fund' as the way of helping with this and developing services. We would want to use the 'change fund' effectively and make sure it is linked to developments outlined in 'partnership in practice' agreements.

Recommendation 4   The Scottish Executive should set up a 'change fund' to help local authorities put in place the recommendations in this review.

Direct payments

37   Since 1997, local authorities have been able to give money directly to people to buy the help they need (if they want and are able to manage the money effectively)[29]. This arrangement is called a **direct payment**. Not many people with learning disabilities have these at the moment. Eleven social work departments have schemes - some are quite new and running as test schemes.

38   Some people and their families or carers do not want the extra responsibility of arranging, paying for and managing services directly. They feel they do not have the knowledge or skills to do that. On the other hand, many are very keen to take more control of their affairs, sometimes with help.

We think **direct payments** should be available to all those who want them. This includes people with **complex needs** who may need the support of an **advocate** to give their views.

39   Despite the small numbers so far, there are some very powerful examples of people getting better focused, more personal and newer services.

An example of good practice

Values into Action are currently promoting **direct payments** becoming more available to people with learning disabilities.

40   It is clear that **direct payments** could play a far bigger role in the future. They can be for one-off payments which would tend to be small but prevent problems by providing a short break or an aid. They could also buy longer-term care services. We need to make sure they are regularly reviewed so that they meet people's changing needs. They could deliver quicker and better outcomes for people's problems. Most importantly, they give people greater control over their care.

Recommendation 5   By 2003, anyone who wants direct payments should be able to have them, and local authorities should be included in the list of possible providers.

A Scottish centre for learning disability

41   In the next few chapters we identify the need for:

- developing advocacy services further;
- appropriate training and support to staff and agencies who work with people with learning disabilities;
- the public to be more aware of learning disabilities; and
- people with learning disabilities to be much more active in the communities in which they live.

42   We considered whether existing organisations could take forward this change alone and decided that we need to create a new organisation to support them. We call this the Scottish centre for learning disability.

43   The main purpose of the centre is to provide a Scotland-wide resource to help the general public and professional staff understand learning disabilities.   The centre should support users, carers and agencies to achieve better outcomes. People with learning disabilities, their families and carers will be members of the joint management committee alongside professionals and academics.

What the centre will be responsible for

44   The centre will offer the following services.

- Consultancy, training and advice to agencies, professionals, staff and others on putting in place the recommendations of this review.
- An advisory and matching service to support local authorities, health boards and others which help those whose needs are so specialised that they cannot be met locally.
- Partnerships with large regional or national enterprises to encourage employment opportunities beyond those provided by individual local authorities.
- High-quality educational materials for:
  - people who use services and their carers to help them follow their goals;
  - academic establishments and staff to raise the overall level of awareness and understanding about learning disabilities;
  - training social care staff in agencies, who plan and provide services for those with learning disabilities; and
  - joint training to share knowledge, understanding and values.
- A programme of public involvement that encourages people in the community to get to know and help people with learning disabilities so that they, too, can enjoy being active citizens.
- Links with national and international research centres to carry out or promote joint research into services for those with learning disabilities.
- Help local services develop new and different practice based on national and international research findings.

The centre will aim to develop advocacy services in local authorities and health boards.

The centre will work with other organisations and add to other recent national initiatives such as the Scottish Accessible Information Forum (SAIF) and the Disability Rights Commission (DRC). Enable, as the national organisation representing people with learning disabilities and their families, has already developed an information and advice service. We consider it essential that the centre uses their expertise in developing their services and also consults other organisations which have an interest in this area such as People First.

45   We expect that either the centre or Enable will maintain and extend the Scottish Executive website.

Recommendation 6   The Scottish Executive should set up a new Scottish centre for learning disability. This would offer advice, training and support to agencies, professionals, people with learning disabilities and parents to bring about the changes we have recommended in this review. The centre will also support the further development of advocacy services.

Scottish service network for autistic spectrum disorders

46   Professionals do not know enough about **autism** and **Asperger's syndrome**. They do not recognise it as often as they should. Early and accurate diagnosis is essential to give people the right help and education to reduce the effect of their disability. Although many children in Scotland are diagnosed before they start school, far fewer people are diagnosed than the research suggests exists[30]. The number of people identified varies widely in different areas as does the knowledge, skill and services. There are not enough facilities for assessing and diagnosing these conditions particularly for older children and adults and in smaller authorities and rural areas. Added to this we were also told that even when there is a diagnosis, services may not be available as no agency sees it as their responsibility to provide them.

47   Some areas have good locally-based services for children but not for adults and other areas have little access to specialist advice and support. The Yorkhill Centre for Autism provides a service for assessing and diagnosing children under 12, although they will provide advice and support to local services for older children. Health boards use this service in different ways.

48   Children of pre-school and primary-school age are usually supported in special schools and special units within **mainstream** schools and in local

services for children and adults. Many services for children and adults with learning disability are not suitable for people with **Asperger's syndrome** whose intellect may not be affected but who have great difficulty in communicating and relating to other people. Some children's services have adapted their environment, routines or staffing levels to make the service 'autism-friendly'. With the right advice and knowledge many others could follow this lead. We also need to see more specialist services for people with **autism**. Voluntary sector organisations specialising in **autism** provide informed and highly-valued support and services for people and their families.

49   To make support for people with an **autistic spectrum disorder** better, local and national priorities must be to:

- continue improving early diagnosis;
- give professionals in local services quick access to information, specialist knowledge, expertise and training;
- widen the range of local support and services available; and
- help people get specialist services quickly when they need them.

50   Looking at models of **managed clinical networks** in the health service, we recommend that those with an interest in this area come together to set up a national service network for children and adults with **autistic spectrum disorders**. The Scottish Society for Autism supported by the National Autistic Society should bring this group together. They should draw up a description of what the national network will do, and when local services should call on it for help. The PIPs should set out how local services will link into the national network. Health boards and local authorities should also identify a named professional within their service who will be responsible for improving local services for people with **autism** and for linking local services to the national network. This may be a local area co-ordinator.

51   Local areas should develop levels of service, such as child care, education, short breaks for carers and social supports based on their best estimate of the number of people with **autistic spectrum disorder** in their area. This estimate should draw on local authority education statistics, research and other information about how many people with an **autistic spectrum disorder** might be expected in a given population. Health boards

and NHS trusts should make sure that GPs, health visitors, school nurses and relevant social services and pre-school staff know about and are trained to use current screening and assessment tools such as the Checklist for Autism in Toddlers (CHAT). Local PIPs should include proposals for how local authorities and their partners will meet the needs of people with an **autistic spectrum disorder** in the area, and cover **mainstream** and specialist services. Agencies should find out how much training front-line staff in their services will need to improve their awareness and understanding of the needs of people with an **autistic spectrum disorder**. They should decide how to deliver the training needed to relevant staff by 2003 and ask the Scottish centre for learning disability to help them with this.

Recommendation 7   The Scottish Society for Autism by working with the National Autistic Society and health boards and local authorities should develop a national network for people with an autistic spectrum disorder.

3 Better choices, stronger voices

1   Better information, communication and **advocacy** are central to making any changes and putting the principles into practice. If we are to include people with learning disabilities fully in our communities, they need to have accurate information so they can make informed choices and decisions about their lives. People with learning disabilities need to be able to have their say. They need to be supported if necessary to make their point. During the review people with learning disabilities and their families made it clear that they wanted to be consulted more and have a greater say in decisions about the support they need to live a full life.

Information for people, professionals and planners

2   Many people using services and their families told us they had trouble finding out what social work, health or other services were available. Families from ethnic-minority backgrounds said there was a serious lack of information available in community languages. In our survey of users and carers quite a few parents said that the only way to find things out was by 'constantly hassling' professionals. People described this process as a 'fight' or a 'battle'.

> 'You have to find out about services for yourself. No-one comes to you automatically to inform you of what services there are, or asks you is there anything you want to know.'

3   Family carers often described other parents as the best source of information and said that professionals did not always take time to listen to or speak to their sons or daughters.

4   Other people said that professionals themselves lacked information and knowledge about learning disabilities, and some professionals acknowledged to us that this was the case. Many primary care and social work staff said they did not have enough training about learning disabilities, and often did not work with enough people with learning disabilities or their families to develop the expertise they needed. Many said they did not always know about the full range of services that might be available in their own area, especially if they were provided by agencies other than their own.

5   The Scottish Executive is currently supporting a number of ideas to improve information for people with disabilities, carers and others.   However, many of these ideas are still at an early stage. The Scottish Accessible Information Forum (SAIF) is being funded to co-ordinate a national strategy to make sure that all information is accessible to people with disabilities, and their carers. Already a new national disability information service 'Update' provides a service to agencies which deal directly with the public. The Social Work Information Review Group (SWIRG) made up of Cosla, the Association of Directors of Social Work, the Accounts Commission and the Scottish Executive is also carrying out a review of information needs for social work in Scotland. The Disability Rights Commission (DRC) will be active in Scotland from April 2000. Enquire, run by Children in Scotland, provides a national advice and information service for families and carers of children with special educational needs.

6   Services to carers will also be widely promoted through the recently launched Strategy for Carers in Scotland. By Spring 2000 the NHS Helpline will be extended to provide information on access to social care services and support for carers, as will NHS Direct when it comes on line.

7   You can already find information through web pages such as Scottish Health on the Web (SHOW) and the Health Education Board for Scotland's website. Social care information will be available through the SHOW site as well as through the NHS Helpline and NHS Direct.

8   Helpful as these initiatives are, none of them provide the one-stop wide-ranging information about local learning disabilities and services that families and carers actually want. There is a danger their needs will be overlooked.

An example of good practice

The Enable family advice service in East Renfrewshire is a local independent service, funded by East Renfrewshire social work department and managed by Enable. It offers clear, accurate, independent information on anything which affects people with learning disabilities and their families in the East Renfrewshire area. It is linked to, and backed by, Enable's national information service but can offer the ongoing face-to-face support and knowledge of local networks and services that individuals and families need.

9   If those who make policies and planners are to provide the services people need, they have to gather better information about the numbers and needs of those with learning disabilities (and their carers) locally, and also crucially, about how well different service options work. As we said earlier, only three areas in Scotland could give us reasonably wide-ranging information about the numbers and needs of people with learning disabilities. Most appear to rely on **prevalence data** to plan services. This is surprising since we were told that all education authorities will know about all children with learning disabilities and children with more **complex needs** will be known to local child health services.

10   People with learning disabilities, their parents and families, professionals, policy-makers and planners all need reliable information of different kinds at different times.

An example of good practice

An example of good practice, FAIR in Edinburgh, provide a range of user-friendly booklets on housing, work, leisure, after-school provision and much more.

People using services need to know:

- where to go and who to ask to get answers to their questions;
- about particular conditions and disabilities and their effects;
- how to get help and who makes decisions about this;
- how professionals carry out assessments and make decisions;
- what social, healthcare and other services and support are available locally, nationally and internationally;
- how to change or challenge professional decisions or complain if they are not happy with what is happening; and
- how to get in touch with other people and families with similar needs and problems.

11   Above all people need a service that is easy to find, easy to understand and where they do not feel passed from 'pillar to post'. We believe people with learning disabilities, their families and carers need a specifically-targeted information service.

Recommendation 8   The Scottish Accessible Information Forum should consult local authorities, health boards and users and carers on how best to provide joint, one-stop, free and accessible local information services for people with learning disabilities, their families and carers. Information must also be available in community languages.

Professionals need to know:

- about the effects of learning disabilities on development and daily living or how to find out about this;
- about up-to-date research, policy and the best way to help people with learning disabilities and their families;
- about good practice and developments in other fields which can be used to care for people with learning disabilities, for example, in rehabilitation or **palliative care** services;
- where they can get the right advice and expertise so they can help families as best they can; and
- where to refer families if they cannot provide help directly.

12   Many professionals need better training before they qualify and after they qualify to improve their knowledge of learning disabilities. They also need access to up-to-date research and to know about local as well as national resources. Much of this could be provided by the Scottish centre for learning disability.

Planners need to know:

- how many people have learning disabilities, or more **complex needs** in their area;
- what the range of needs is likely to be;
- whether this is likely to change in future and why;
- how many people with learning disabilities currently use their services;
- how much services cost; and
- how well different service options work and what people think of them.

Planners should work with others, both within local authority departments and across agencies so that any information they gather can be shared.

13   Local authorities and health boards need to work together to improve and develop the information they currently have about the numbers and needs of people with learning disabilities and their families and carers. Setting up the local registers we refer to in chapter 2 will help this process.

Recommendation 9   The first PIP agreements should set out how local authorities, health boards and primary care trusts will set up and maintain local registers.

Communication

14   At least 50% of people with learning disabilities have significant communication problems with up to 80% having some communication difficulties[31]. People who find it hard to make their views known because their speech is impaired, or who use different ways of communicating, need skilled and regular help from speech and language therapists. Yet users and carers told us that it was very hard to get these services.

15   Communication is central to being included in society. People with learning disabilities and their families may need help to communicate their views and their knowledge. The starting point must be that professionals can communicate clearly and in ways that make it easy for people to understand them.

16   People with learning disabilities need time, help and sometimes independent advice and support to put across their views. People with more **complex needs** are most likely to have difficulty in expressing their views. Communication with them may mean a great deal of support is needed and may be very slow. More positive efforts may need to be made to involve them and their families. Professionals may need help from families and carers to make communication possible in many circumstances. Families and carers may need to make the time, and will sometimes need outside help, to make their communication with their family member as good as it can be.

17   Speech and language therapists are an important resource in helping to develop communication. They sometimes work with a **clinical engineer** to do this. Other professionals also contribute, such as educational and clinical psychologists, as well as art, music and drama therapists.

We were told:

> 'It's important you take time to listen – not only to our words. Some people have difficulty with words.'

18   Scottish Ministers in their response to the Riddell Committee[32] suggested that the Scottish Executive would review with Cosla and relevant health agencies the use and effectiveness of current funding in relation to speech and language therapy for children. We believe that also needs to include adults.

Recommendation 10 The Scottish Executive's review of the effectiveness of funding speech and language therapy for children should also include services for adults.

Advocacy

19   Many people with learning disabilities, their carers and professionals recognise that an independent person standing up for the person with a learning disability can help find the right solutions to very difficult problems. Although **advocacy** is now more widely available, our survey of users and carers found that it did not play a large part in people's lives. This suggests that there is a significant gap in the range of support available.

20   Advocacy allows people to have a greater say in decisions which affect their lives. People with learning disabilities find it useful, and they enjoy the company and friendship that their **advocates** often offer. A user in our survey said:

> 'I just know her – she is my friend. I meet my friend, go out places … Ellen is there and Ellen helps me.'

The review found that very few people with learning disabilities have access to an **advocate**.

21   Research shows that people with **complex needs** are more at risk of a wide range of poor outcomes. These include:

- less choice about their lives;
- less involvement socially;

- fewer chances of employment;
- less active lifestyles; and
- greater health needs[33, 34] .

They are most likely to have difficulty expressing their needs and as a result need more help.

22   National guidance on **advocacy** covers the types and benefits of **advocacy** and factors to consider in getting advocacy services started[35]. The guidance is as relevant to improving the lives of people with learning disabilities as other care groups and the review recommends it to organisations which commission and plan services. The Scottish Executive has sponsored further work on **commissioning** and supporting independent advocacy services which it will issue in the near future[36].

23   **Advocacy** can take different forms. Many people with learning disabilities want to be able to speak up more for themselves. They would like to be trained to represent themselves or others. **Citizen advocacy** is when a committed person supports a person with a learning disability. **Advocacy** needs to be more widely available. We need to build towards a position where everyone who has **complex needs** or is particularly vulnerable has ready access to an **advocate**.

Recommendation 11   The Scottish Executive should continue to encourage the development of local independent advocacy services.

4 A full life - where you live

Where we are now

1   As we said in chapter 1, the number of people with learning disabilities generally has increased by over 1% each year over the last 35 years. Estimates suggest that there are about 120,000 people with learning disabilities in Scotland (up to 20,000 with severe disabilities), compared with 83,000 (and 13,000 with severe disabilities) about 35 years ago. This trend will continue for at least another 10 years. As a result more people are living with their families or on their own and can access local services, in the community. This means that these local services are being asked to meet needs more than ever before.

2   Most children and adults with learning disabilities live with their own families. The number reduces as they get older but many still live with their families in middle age. A small number already live in their own homes. In 1998, just under 2,450 people with learning disabilities still lived in hospitals[37]. About 4,800 lived in residential care or nursing homes for people with learning disabilities[38, 39]. About 600 lived in settings with good visiting support[40]. The range of those supported living options has increased a great deal in recent years.

3   The numbers of people in hospital have reduced from nearly 6,500 in 1980 to fewer than 2,450 in 1998 (an estimated 2,200[41] in 1999) and they are still going down[42].   There are now 25, mostly small, hospital sites. Two (with 360 places) have Ministerial approval to close. Firm proposals to close sites apply to another 950 places and sites with a further 350 places are gradually being scaled down when appropriate replacement services, care and accommodation are set up. (There is no timetable for this action.) In the short term, on health boards' current plans, the largest institutions will close by the end of 2002, leaving about 700 to 800 places in total. The larger sites include Merchiston (179), Kirklands (179), Craig Phadrig (53), Strathmartine (99) and Ayrshire and Arran (110).

4   Reducing the number of around 4,000 people in hospital has been broadly matched by an increase in the number of people in nursing or residential care homes. This group now make up 66% of total residents, compared with 14% in 1980. And, about 600 people now live in informal supported accommodation. This suggests that while many more people now live in less institutionalised forms of care, the increase in the number of

people with learning disabilities in Scotland has been supported by community-based, rather than hospital or residential or nursing home services. In neither case does this mean that people in the community are living as independent lives as possible.

Where we want to be

5   In future, both children and adults with learning disabilities should, wherever possible, be supported to lead a full life with their families or in their own homes. Some people may be best in a setting which is not an ordinary house owned or rented by them or their family. But whatever it is, it should allow them to live a full life and be included in society while providing privacy and allowing them to develop. Hospitals are not places where people with learning disabilities can live full lives. We asked someone we met in hospital what he wanted out of life. He said:

'Somewhere decent to live, a job, some friends – the same as you really.'

6   What would supported living look like which successfully promotes choice and independence? We surveyed examples in Scotland, and paid for research on the position in other parts of the world[43, 44]. People want the following.

Choice of bricks and mortar

People want a full range of housing options in which they may live in groups or on their own with support. Supported individual or joint tenancies and 'assisted home ownership' are popular.

An example of good practice

Home Ownership

Home ownership is a good option for some people with learning disabilities. Ownership Options in Scotland:

- helps people with disabilities overcome barriers;
- provides a consultancy service,
- provides financial help and advice;
- arranges maintenance and is a link between those looking for property and potential buyers.

To make the decisions about where to live

Housing solutions should be based on discussing them with the person with a learning disability.

A network of active support

This should come from staff on site, **peripatetic support staff** or local **domiciliary services**, to help individuals live in the community.

An example of good practice

Flexible, person-centred care planning

Inclusion Glasgow's packages of care include a one-off resource to support people immediately after they leave hospital. The organisation place the agreed funding for the person in a bank account, known as the service fund. How the fund is managed and used is decided in the person's plan. They can spend it on care at home, in work or for leisure pursuits. Out of 28 people who used to be in Lennox Castle, all have their own home, seven own them and some have jobs. None has returned to hospital. As planned, **natural supports** and networks play a more significant part in the overall pattern of support, and the cost of the care package should reduce.

Flexibility

The people being supported will change. Some will become frailer and some moving into the community will respond positively to a change of environment and begin to be less dependent. Services need to adapt to people's needs as they change.

To build links with neighbours and the community

We cannot separate accommodation from other areas of support for daily living. This should include considering how to help people form neighbourly relationships and use local services.

An example of good practice

Community placements

Placement with families has been a small but important part of the programme of resettling people from Lynebank Hospital. These placements can be either short or long-term, or for respite care. Evidence suggests that individuals have more access to people and activities in the community through being part of a family. It is also cost-effective.

Consultation

People need to take part in consultation to inform strategic planning for housing services.

7   This chapter recognises the growing pressures on local authorities and others to meet, appropriately, the accommodation and care needs of an ever-growing population of people with learning disabilities who live in the community. It also recognises the need to provide supported living options for most people currently in long-stay hospitals or care homes. Change is necessary at a number of levels, some of which will have greater priority than others. Supporting people better in the community and closing long-stay hospitals must come before the much more gradual shift from care homes to supported living. This will cost money, but we have to judge the benefits to people against that cost.

How do we get there

8   Two pieces of research on the costs and benefits of different support models have been or are about to be published. One compares the costs and values of housing, residential campuses on NHS sites and village communities[45]. The other compares the costs of a variety of settings, for people with low, moderate, high and intensive needs

9   These studies show the relative total costs and the benefits of a range of options. The table below, based on these studies, shows the range of costs according to need. Comparing costs is not always what might be expected (partly because of the limited size of the sample). Options providing

independence and choice cost more for people with intensive needs, but may cost less for others with lower levels of need. Adult placements consistently cost less across the range of needs.

Figure 2   Total costs of different types of care

Type of support	Low	Moderate	High	Intensive
Self-contained independent (including supported living)	-	-	£22,059	£59,242
Self-contained network (see note 1 below)	£20,172	-	£29,186	£58,199
Single-site cluster (see note 2 below)	£22,494	£20,495	£37,444	£53,878
Small shared (2 to 4 people)	£31,446	-	£33,672	£50,038
Large shared (5 or more people)	-	-	£39,790	£51,477
Adult placement	-	£18,174	£21,659	£29,665

Note 1 This **mainstream** housing is usually self-contained and linked with other accommodation through a shared support service.

Note 2 This is group units of accommodation on a single-site, with support usually from a specific team.

10   By comparison, a nursing home place in Scotland costs about £21,000 each year and a residential place about £26,000 each year. The total cost of a hospital place is about £45,000. This cost is higher because of some non-recurring, double-running costs.

11   These studies bring out three main messages. First, on a range of measures, NHS residential campuses offered poorer-quality outcomes than housing. Second, costs vary significantly from model to model, both within and between categories of special needs. Carefully matching individual needs with the model of care is essential in terms of both care and costs. Third, although small group living costs more than living in larger groups, it

has considerable advantages for people with learning disabilities. These advantages include:

- better staffing;
- a reduction in the use of anti-psychotic medication;
- an increase in access to independent advocacy;
- an increase in choices for residents;
- an increase in becoming involved more socially;
- an increase in hours of scheduled activities during the day; and
- an increase in the number of recreational and community-based activities.

12   Better outcomes also rely on other factors for example:

- carefully assessing and planning for, the needs of the person;
- the choices available being clearly presented to the individual, their carer or **advocate**; and
- support staff being trained to help the person live in the community.

13   The research evidence and indeed local authorities' own best-value reviews point broadly towards the benefits of supported living as opposed to residential care. Older people (75 and over) with learning disabilities who have spent a large part of their lives in a long-stay hospital may consider a move to a nursing home. As with others what the person prefers is important in making the decision. But for younger people, other solutions are best.

14   Recognising people's changing needs is important. The support individuals need in the community will, in some cases, reduce as their experience and confidence grows. In other cases needs will increase. As a result of this, the cost of the support will change.

15   In coming to decisions on the best care option for each person, local authorities should fully take account of:

- the costs of various care options;
- the possibility that people's need for support may well reduce as they settle into their new lives or may increase as they grow older; and
- the benefits to the individual of supported living options.

People already living in the community

16   Most people with learning disabilities live in their own or family homes in the community. They and their families will have new or changing needs and expectations in future.   Young adults may want to move to a home of their own. Younger parents may increasingly expect their child to live independently, whereas older parents may be more concerned about who will look after their child when they die.   Others may not have the right package of housing and support to help them live properly in the community.

17   Some will benefit from other changes proposed in the review, such as better respite care and **direct payments** which give better and more flexible care. If they need a new or extended package of housing and care we expect agencies to provide this in line with the aims of the review. Our user and carer survey, submissions and other sources all confirmed these pressures, but did not put a cost to them.   However, they are probably the greatest priority. We would want to use any 'change fund' to make progress.

Providing services in the community instead of long-stay hospitals

18   Learning disability hospitals have provided a resource for people, often with **complex needs** or who are statutorily **detained**, because it would not be possible to support them in their own home or in local community settings. They also provide short-stay assessment and treatment facilities, respite care, **palliative care** for people with gradually worsening conditions (such as Down's syndrome combined with dementia), and day care.

19   We decided that people's homes should not be in hospitals. Hospitals are not appropriate settings for social care, and they are not necessary settings for most healthcare. Over the next five years, services should be built up in the community to allow the long-stay hospitals which are left to close by March 2005.

Recommendation 12   Health boards should make sure they have plans now for closing all remaining long-stay hospitals for people with learning disabilities by 2005.

20   However, we will need to keep a small number of in-patient places for some people with learning disabilities.

These will be for the following people.

- Those whose need for specialised or complex health assessment or treatment cannot be met in the community (probably not more than 150 to 200 people in Scotland). We will need clear conditions for using these facilities to make sure that people with learning disabilities move on from them to more appropriate care settings as soon as possible.
- People on statutory orders (currently 178), some of whom will be offenders with mental health problems. The government is currently reviewing the law on these cases and proposals are currently out for consultation. Changing the law may lead to other care options.
- A small number of people whose treatment may be lengthy or who need a more supportive setting for a long period.

21   We estimate that we may need a *total* of 300-400 places across Scotland to cater for those needing in-patient assessment and treatment and, under the present law, those on statutory orders. We believe there will be an increased need for assessment and treatment places as long-stay hospitals close.

22   Local authorities and health boards should meet the **continuing care** needs of people with learning disabilities, as far as possible, in their own homes or in small domestic settings in their own communities. They need to develop ways to improve joint working to make sure they meet health needs, where possible, outside hospital.

Recommendation 13   **Health boards should aim to reduce their assessment and treatment places specifically for people with learning disabilities to four for every 100,000 population across the country as a whole. Health boards should plan for appropriate community services to avoid in-patient assessments and treatment.**

23   As long-stay hospitals and homes are closed, health boards should transfer part of this cost to local authorities who will become responsible for the care needs. Health boards will hold back an element for health services in the community. Local authorities will pay any extra social care costs from the increasing resources made available to them for their social work services (£1.1 billion in 1999-2000).

24   Under their existing financial plans, by 2002, health boards and local authorities will have resettled most of those living in long-stay hospitals in 1998. However, to close long-stay hospitals will mean losing another 700 to 800 places from 2002 to 2005. Bridging costs to the NHS for 800 places might amount to about £9 million a year (about £35,000 for each place) over that period. Health boards' general allocations include an amount for the costs of moving people as hospitals scale down and new services are added in the community.

Recommendation 14   Health Boards with sites remaining after 2002 should develop, with their partners, other services in the community as a priority and set aside resources to meet these costs. This will feature in planning guidance and the boards' performance management arrangements.

An example of good practice

Gogarburn Hospital, a long-stay hospital on the outskirts of Edinburgh, is the first of its type to close in May 1999. Those involved needed:

- new resources if residents were to enjoy a better quality of life;
- a pact of the four councils, the health board, the NHS trust, Scottish Homes and housing associations and the voluntary sector to create a structured approach;
- a wide range of solutions to meet people's needs;
- tight control and a strong financial structure (deciding what the financial limits are at the beginning and managing them);
- to create new systems through ideas such as **benchmarking**, to achieve better use of resources, better relationships with providers and better targeted services for users;
- clear communication between agencies and patients, relatives and staff; and
- a wide-ranging staff plan.

25   In considering how to provide for the 700 to 800 people who will still be in hospital in 2002 (less those who need assessment and treatment and those on statutory orders) local authorities will need to recognise that while some residents will be older and so more likely to be suited to nursing or care homes, most will need more imaginative options.

26   We became aware, during the review, that local authorities are having some difficulty in arranging supported living options. Nursing homes are being used more and more, partly for economic reasons. And significant numbers of people who expected to leave hospital to go to supported living are now moving into large group homes or nursing homes. We think this should be avoided wherever possible.

27   The total cost (including healthcare costs in the community) of providing a mix of adult placements, small group homes, supported living and nursing or care homes would be £17.3 million for 400 people. This would compare with the recurring hospital costs for 400 people of about £15 million (see appendix 4). New hospital places might require **capital** of about £18 to 25 million over three years. Some of this may be paid for using the proceeds of selling sites. Other **capital** charges may be about £1.5 million each year.

28   So if we take **revenue**, **capital** and **bridging finance** together, the cost of providing for 700 to 800 people in the community less the 300 to 400 who will stay in the NHS will be about:

- £2 million of extra **revenue** each year for local authorities by year three;
- £1.5 million for other **capital** charges (NHS);
- £9 million over three years of non-recurring **bridging finance** (NHS);
- £6 million **capital** for housing, spread over the three years[46]; and
- £18 to 25 million of health **capital**, spread over three years, which could be paid for using the proceeds of selling sites.

The NHS would still fund the other 300 to 400 places, at a cost of around £15 million each year.

Healthcare for people leaving long-stay hospitals

29   We should meet the general healthcare needs of people with learning disabilities in the same settings as the rest of the population. We should meet specialist needs related to their disability in the least restrictive setting possible, and ideally in the community.

30   Hospitals currently oversee the day-to-day medical and health needs of residents, including screening. Developing services in the community, including health services, is the way ahead. This means developing a new structure to assess and support people in different settings, including people with more **complex needs**. Some are already in place and working effectively. Trained nurses are working alongside social care staff in a person's own home or in other community settings. Some areas have developed plans, supported by training, to allow non-health staff to give medication and carry out other health-related tasks.

31   Extra support for people with **challenging behaviour** or offending behaviour has also led to more people being able to live in the community and use **mainstream** services. These are good examples of developing links between learning disabilities, other specialist services and older people, mental health and physical disability services, and they lead to our relying less on sending people into hospitals. We look at primary and general healthcare again in chapter 6.

Making sure there is quality for people living in care homes

32   For some people, nursing home or residential care will be appropriate forms of care. We are improving the quality of care in both these and other settings. The Scottish Executive is committed to setting up a new organisation, the Scottish Commission for the Regulation of Care (SCRC) in 2001 to make sure the quality of care wherever it is provided is consistent. This applies in someone's own home, in a care home, or in supported living. The Scottish Executive has set up a National Care Standards Committee to draw up national standards for care in all these settings, with people's quality of life as the central focus.   But whatever the setting, quality has to be determined from the inside, rather than enforced from the outside.   It has to be part of planning services, and providing and monitoring them.

33   The emphasis on including people in society, and on continuing development applies equally to residential or nursing home care. Individual solutions, based on individual needs and choices, should always be the aim.

34   Some local authorities are already examining the role and functions of residential care, most of which is provided by the voluntary sector.   One has carried out a best-value study.   Its conclusions point broadly in the same

direction as our review, in other words helping people stay in supported living. However, achieving the better outcomes will be more expensive. There will also be costs involved in getting there.

35   We expect change in two ways. First, people who used to go into residential care (about 400[47] each year) or nursing homes (unknown, but quite small) will instead be placed in other forms of accommodation, wherever possible. Second, as part of the change of direction locally, some people will move out of residential care or nursing homes to more suitable settings. We see this as a gradual process based on considering the availability of suitable accommodation and support locally. Local authorities and health boards need to include people with learning disabilities currently living in homes for other care groups in these considerations.

36   About 1,800 people classed as being in a 'residential home' already live in supported accommodation of different sorts. Over time, and recognising the local nature of these considerations, we expect to see a shift to the pattern of care. We expect:

- considerably fewer people (including older people) in nursing homes; and
- most people in various forms of supported accommodation, with particular emphasis on adult placements, small group homes and supported living arrangements.

37   This review has given a lead on the direction we want to travel. Decisions about the need for, scale and pace of any shifts are best left for local decisions.

38   There will be some extra costs, but also benefits for people. This is one of the areas where a 'change fund' would clearly be a good idea. We discuss this more fully in chapter 2.

5 A full life - what you do

1   This chapter looks at the value of good-quality and stimulating day opportunities and short breaks for people with learning disabilities and their families. It ends with a section which highlights the need for the general public to understand more about learning disabilities.

2   Support for people with learning disabilities, whatever its focus, must strengthen their ability to make their own contribution. This may be either to their community, their family, or their workplace. Those who work with people with learning disabilities need to build on what each individual can do to make a real difference to their quality of life.

Day opportunities - Where we are now

3   Day care costs local authorities about £53 million each year[48]. The number of people with learning disabilities going to social day centres has grown from 4,400 in 1980 to 8,300 in 1998[49]. A place costs about £7,000 a year. In March 1998, hospitals had 270[50] day places for 489 people, at a cost of just under £2 million[51].

4   93% of people going to day centres do not have paid work[52]. Only 20% of activity in day centres takes the form of education and employment, while 28% involves leisure and recreation[53]. Similarly, only 25% of sheltered workshop spending goes on learning disabilities[54].

5   We learned of people going to day centres for many years without a formal assessment. Most people using services who were interviewed as part of our user and carer survey described day centres as boring and lacking in direction. However, they did value the chance to access health services and to meet friends.

6   Carers' perspectives may be different. Day services give them valuable opportunities to follow other interests, education or work. Carers are understandably concerned at any suggestion that services might be taken away, and their own opportunities restricted. It would be pointless if new developments place heavier burdens on family carers.

7   Many day services for adults are not focused enough on continuous learning and development. Day care is not seen as a stepping stone to new experiences or to employment. It does not challenge and stimulate each person enough.

8   That said, a number of people with **complex needs**, but particularly those with **multiple** and **profound disabilities** and some people with **autistic spectrum disorders**, will continue to need structured day opportunities. Some day services provide high-quality care and involve people with **profound** and **multiple disabilities** in everyday activities in the community (with support). Health boards need to consider developing more outreach services for people in these settings.

An example of good practice

The Aveyron day centre was set up by a parents' group and now receives funding from South Lanarkshire social work department. It provides day care for up to 18 people many of whom have other physical disabilities, severe health problems, **sensory impairment** or **challenging behaviour**. The local community learning disability team work closely with centre staff to support those who go to the centre.

The future scope of day services

9   Day opportunities are important to people with learning disabilities. But traditional day services are no longer appropriate descriptions of the ways in which people with learning disabilities want to spend their days. They value a structured day, especially one with meaningful activities.

10   People with learning disabilities want fuller lives, and to be able to join in more with others in the community. Services need to be more flexible and meet people's needs if this is to happen. Local authorities need to look at their current day care services to see how they can include people more in the community.

An example of good practice

The Carisbrooke day centre provides day care for those with significant physical and health needs. There are close links with primary care and specialist health services.

11   The role of day centres should change. They should increasingly become resource centres, offering only some in-house activities and support. They need to use more community resources and help people with learning disabilities get continuing education and development, real jobs and more involved in sport and leisure activities. Community education also has an important part to play. Local authorities are currently drawing up their first community learning plans which have to include the needs of people with learning disabilities. Nobody should go to a day centre full time, but they could use it as a base to identify and go to activities in the wider community. In some areas day activities can come to the person (for example, one-to-one outreach), or to a group.

12   Local authorities will want to give particular care and attention to how day opportunities can meet the needs of people with **multiple** and **profound disabilities** or those who may not be able to benefit from employment or continuing education. Opportunities will vary from person to person but need to focus on personal and social development. Services will need to be available for people with specific and other health needs. Good day opportunities are particularly valuable to people who have **challenging behaviour**[55]. Organisations will need to provide appropriate staff training to support these changes.

An example of good practice

The White Top Centre in Dundee provides day care for 15 people with **profound** and **multiple**, physical and learning disabilities. The centre opened in 1994 with funding from a charitable trust and is now supported by Dundee social work department. Tayside health board pay for some health posts. Nursing, physiotherapy and social care staff work together to support those who use the centre and their families.

13   Local authorities need to review their day care services. In doing so, they will want to be sensitive to the anxieties and views of users and carers. They need to balance the needs of users and carers so that they help the person with disabilities and prevent family breakdown. Good personal planning for the person with learning disabilities will take full account of the needs of their carer.

14   Local authorities should be able to use existing resources better by taking advantage of services and opportunities in the community and looking for real jobs. This is an approach already used in many areas which are successfully remodelling services. However, changing the current style and shape of services will take time. Extra money from a 'change fund' would help to make that shift.

Recommendation 15   Local authorities and health boards, should both examine what they provide and develop more modern, flexible and responsive services which support people in the community through employment, lifelong learning and getting them involved socially. Day healthcare services for people with learning disabilities should be mixed with those in the community.

New opportunities for lifelong learning and development

15   Lifelong learning is important to people's development and provides opportunities for people to feel more included. The Higher Still Programme provides a framework for people of all abilities, from those with profound learning difficulties through to those sitting Advanced Higher. So, it could offer young people with disabilities excellent opportunities for lifelong learning.

16   Many people with learning disabilities already take part in educational activities within day centres and in further education. There is a lot more scope for continuing education to play a bigger part in their development. Well-planned learning opportunities can have significant and long-lasting effects. They can improve the quality of life for people with learning disabilities and help them to take advantage of other activities and employment. They can also help them to develop independent living skills so that they rely less on others.

17   The main recommendation of the Beattie Committee is that **post school education** should aim to include more people. This should mean that it is better designed and delivered to meet the needs, abilities and hopes of young people within a supportive environment. What is provided should match needs rather than asking the young person to adapt to the learning environment.

18   Adults with learning disabilities, like any other adults, need learning opportunities throughout their lives. They want to learn skills for work, enjoy leisure activities, improve their skills (especially communication) develop self-confidence and **self-advocacy**, and learn to use facilities in their local communities.

19   Most further education colleges are now controlled by new boards of management. They have an important contribution to make to post school learning. Colleges, training providers and local authority community learning services should work together to make sure that an imaginative range of opportunities is available. They should work with those who provide other services to make sure that learning is relevant to the individual and consistent with the needs assessment and 'personal life plan'.

20   The Beattie Committee asked the Learning Disability Review to consider whether their proposed National Action Group should set up a challenge fund to support and test work on improving access to continuing learning for those who need a lot of support. We approve of this recommendation, but would want to widen the opportunity to access continuing learning to *all* people with learning disabilities. The Director of our proposed Scottish centre for learning disability should be a member of Beattie's proposed National Action Group to make sure the voice of people with learning disabilities is heard on employment issues at a national level.

Developing employment opportunities

21   Many people with disabilities want a decent job. They want to get on in life and have friends at work. The Scottish Executive's **social inclusion** strategy ranks having a job high in the list of measures to help people to be included in society. Employment has, so far, rarely been an option for people with learning disabilities. If they are to be usefully included in society, that has to change.

22   During the course of the review we heard about some very successful employment projects. Many of these have been created by the voluntary sector, for example, Enable in Paisley. Others include Jobs 4 All, a not-for-profit recruitment agency for people with disabilities run by North Highland College, and North Lanarkshire Council's Supported Employment project. They focus on helping people with learning disabilities get real jobs. The

Employment Disability Unit in Dundee has had considerable success with a job club, a sheltered placement scheme and a work experience programme. We met people who had gone to day centres for over 20 years and who are now satisfactorily in full-time jobs. Unfortunately there are only a few of these projects. One person told us:

'I keep on being assessed for employment but never get a job.'

23 The New Deal for Disabled People is experimenting with new ideas. Personal adviser services will be the first step in transforming the way in which the benefits system supports disabled people who want to work.

24 Many employment projects centre around employment development workers. They need a broad range of skills from negotiating and marketing, to offering on-the-job support and training, and working with parents and others. They match the employee to a job and train and help him or her into employment. They also provide gradually-reducing support in that employment. Some New Deal for Disabled People pilot schemes include development workers. The responsibility on the employer is to treat and support their employee with learning disabilities in exactly the same way as any other. Those who employ people with learning disabilities have shown they value them.

25 Employment development workers should:

- work towards including people with learning disabilities in ordinary work settings;
- help people find jobs which offer the same pay, terms and conditions as employees doing the same kind of work;
- offer people the necessary support to be able to work on their own, with appropriate risk assessment and management; and
- help those with **complex needs** to find work and provide ongoing support where necessary.

26 However, real jobs may not be everyone's aim. Opportunities also have to be found for 'tasters', part-time opportunities and voluntary activities. There is still a place for sheltered workshops. Whatever the setting, the aim ought to be to help the person develop, and wherever possible to get them fully involved in society.

27   Employing people with learning disabilities or arranging it is not the responsibility of any single agency. Agencies involved in care, health, employment, benefits and indeed in the business world need to work together. As we mentioned earlier, the Beattie Committee is proposing a National Action Group. But it is likely to consider strategies and practical approaches to developing employment, for example, in promoting social firms which help young people move into employment. We suggest that Enable, as the national organisation for people with learning disabilities, should contribute to this work. And, local authorities and health boards could give a lead to local employers by taking on more people with learning disabilities.

28   Supporting people into employment offers them the opportunity to be included, to gain more self-esteem and to meet new people. It can also be cost effective for authorities, compared to the cost of day care (£7,000 for each place each year). Moreover, once the support is withdrawn, local authorities can use that same resource for someone else. In terms of comparing other costs, we were told that a 'Training for Work' place costs about £3,200, and that the Department of Employment will pay up to £4,760 for a full-time worker on a supported employment scheme. So, there can be advantages for people and local authorities in following-up employment led solutions.

Recommendation 16   Local authorities need to give much greater priority to developing a range of employment opportunities for people with learning disabilities. And, with health boards those authorities should lead by example in employing more people with learning disabilities.

Enough money to join in?

29   Benefits play a big part in the lives of people with learning disabilities. Most are not, or have not been, wage earners, and benefits are often their only source of income. So their ability to lead a normal and fulfilling life is governed by benefits. Making the most of income from benefits is an important part of the Scottish Executive's plan to include more people in society.

30   Some benefits provide a source of income for everyday living expenses (Severe Disablement Allowance, Income Support, Housing Benefit, Incapacity

Benefit and so on). Benefits also help people who may be able to work to gain employment. There are a number of New Deal initiatives to help people on long-term Incapacity Benefits move into work. These include the following.

- Increasing the therapeutic earnings limit in Incapacity Benefit and Severe Disablement Allowance to £58 a week from April 1999. Disabled people who carry out therapeutic work can then benefit from the national minimum wage.

- Introducing a 12-month linking rule for people on long-term incapacity benefits in October 1998 to reassure them that they can try work without losing out if they fall ill again.

- Removing the 16-hour restriction on the amount of voluntary work that people can do who receive incapacity benefits.

- Piloting (for a year from April 1999) a package of four measures in 15 areas (including south-west Scotland, Grampian and Lanarkshire) to help people with disabilities who want to return to work. The pilot allow those on incapacity benefits to earn a small amount of money (up to £15) without losing benefit; and to try out a job for a trial period while still on benefit. They also allow access to a Jobmatch payment of £50 a week for people moving into part-time work; and a Jobfinder's Grant of £200 for those starting full-time work.

31   Users and carers told us that the New Deal for Disabled People is still in pilot form. Unfortunately, since most people with learning disabilities do not get Jobseeker's Allowance, they cannot join the main scheme. However, the experience of the few people with learning disabilities who have been able to get through the system suggests it is effective in helping get them into employment.

32   Benefits also help with the other costs of disability. The Independent Living Fund (ILF) is a trust fund which can make discretionary grants. It can make life better for some people by supporting independent living. People do not always understand why some people get it and others do not. More specifically, the limit on earnings for support under ILF may have had a negative effect on getting people to work. For that reason, the Government has increased the limit they can ignore on earnings under the fund.

33   People who have been in care homes since 1993 and have preserved rights to higher DSS benefits are worried about moving to other housing options. The Department of Health and the Department of Social Security are

currently looking at the effects on local authorities if they have preserved rights cases transferred to them.

34   A person's ability to make financial decisions for themselves is often governed by the decisions of others. For instance, someone in a registered home would have their care and accommodation costs paid for, but would be left with only a small income for them to use. The same person in a supported living setting could be left with much more choice about how to use this money. Charging policies can eat away personal income in accommodation which is not registered. Different decisions on Housing Benefit at a local level can lead to different outcomes for people.

35   The benefits system is complicated and getting the right advice and help is essential. The range and level of benefits varies considerably according to personal circumstances. The research paper we commissioned identifies some of the difficulties people face in getting benefits[56]. People with learning disabilities and their representatives told us repeatedly that they found the benefits system difficult to understand and to find their way around.

Recommendation 17   The Scottish Executive should consider raising, with the Department of Social Security, specific areas of concern related to benefits and support for people with learning disabilities.

Leisure and recreation

36   Leisure and recreation are important to all of us, and we do not all like to do the same things. This is also true of people with learning disabilities. Currently about 28% of activity in day care takes the form of leisure and recreation inside and outside day centres. Much of this time is spent with others who have learning disabilities.

37   A better approach would be for people to mix with others of their own age and interests in the community. If these links do not exist at the moment, agencies need to encourage and develop them. Befriending schemes can help with this. People with learning disabilities need to be involved in activities enjoyed by the public generally. They need to use public facilities more alongside non-disabled people, with less segregated sessions, events, shows and activities. In reviewing their day care opportunities local authorities should consider developing befriending schemes and links with other community groups.

Transport

38   Getting around means a lot to people with learning disabilities. During our review it became clear that they are not satisfied with local transport services. Improving transport for people with learning disabilities means:

- for the less able, having access to special transport for care and social activities;
- for those who are more able, making more use of public transport (either on their own or with others), wherever possible; and
- having a transport system which meets people's needs.

39   Developments such as the Scottish Executive's rural transport initiative are helping certain areas, but we think we need better transport networks generally. There are already arrangements in place within Scotland and the Department of the Environment, Transport and the Regions (DETR) on issues such as access.

40   Training drivers is also important. DETR issued guidance in 1997, 'Taking Care of Your Passengers', and bus operators throughout the country have just issued a video 'It's a Bloody Nuisance' related to the needs of people with disabilities. Closer to home, the Scottish Executive is shortly publishing a research study, 'Transport Provision for Disabled People in Scotland', which identifies gaps in the current system and recommendations for action, locally and nationally. This offers a new opportunity to look at concerns in Scotland.

41   Timetables need to be very clear if people are to understand them. And, bus drivers need to realise what the needs of people with learning disabilities are, which may not be obvious. To overcome this, one group has produced a small card explaining that the holder has a learning disability, and inviting the driver to remember this. It has been widely welcomed by both drivers and users and is a good example of an effective idea which is relatively cheap to put into practice.

Recommendation 18   **Local authorities should review their local transport services, to make sure that people with learning disabilities can use public services wherever possible.**

The importance of short breaks – where we are now

42   Most people spend time away from their parents and families. They go to school, they visit relatives and friends, and spend time with other people, doing different things. Children have tea or stay overnight at a friend's home, adults may see friends, partners or colleagues outside their own home, go to leisure facilities or clubs, or do evening classes. People with learning disabilities, and their families often need help to arrange these simple but very important matters. One carer told us:

> 'Fun, interesting activities, making friends her own age, are the most important things for my daughter. I need to know she is happy and secure.'

43   Research on respite care suggests that what is offered is directed more at carers' needs rather than the needs of people with disabilities[57]. Many families are unhappy with the term 'respite', and prefer to use 'short breaks' which shows that the services should be designed to meet both sets of needs.

44   Where families have access to a short break service they value it highly, but they report they rarely receive enough to meet their needs. While the number of services providing short breaks has grown a great deal over recent years, they are still not meeting the demand[58]. And the effort needed to actually get a short break can be tiresome. We were told:

> 'It's a performance trying to book respite.'

45   The number of children with learning disabilities in **mainstream** and specialist education in September 1998 was 8,800, but there is no record of the numbers within this group who need or actually receive short breaks[59]. The Accounts Commission produces information about the numbers of *all* children with disabilities in each local authority who received respite care at least once. They found that out of 3,800 children assessed (in 1997-98) as needing a respite place, 3,300 actually got one[60]. Because these figures include children with other types of disability, it is not possible to give the exact number of children with learning disabilities who actually received respite care. These figures also do not include those whose needs are not assessed. We do know that where new respite for children has been developing it tends to focus on the needs of children with learning disabilities[61].

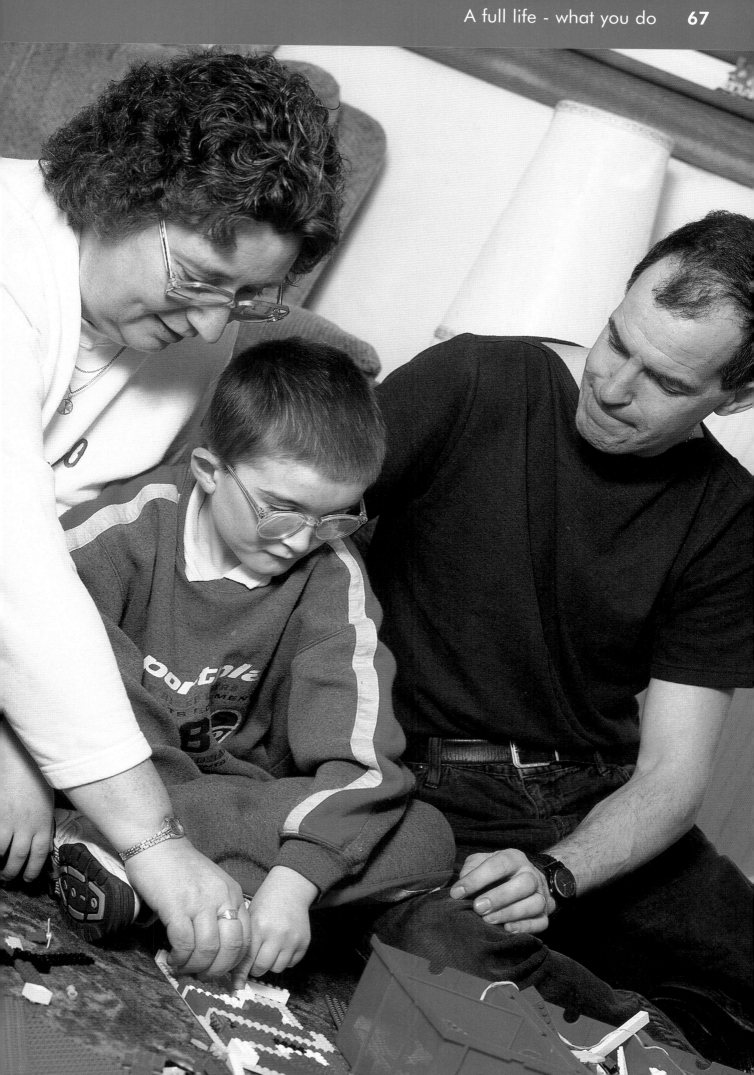

46   The Accounts Commission also produces figures for adults with learning disabilities in each authority who received respite care at least once. These tell us that the number of short breaks provided across Scotland varies a great deal. For instance, an adult with learning disabilities in one area is 11 times more likely to get a short break than someone in another. Overall in 1997-98, out of 3,600 adults assessed who needed a short break 3,200 got a service. Again it is relevant to note these figures do not include those whose needs are not assessed.

47   Using long-stay hospitals for respite for people with learning disabilities continues to grow. Out of 4,100 people with learning disabilities who went into hospital in the year to March 31 1998, 3,400 people went for holidays and respite. A sizeable number were children. (However, it is likely some people will have been counted twice as some may have had more than one period of respite care during this time[62].) As long-stay hospitals run down, local authorities and health boards will need to provide appropriate alternatives in the community. And, many general hospitals continue to provide respite for children in long-term paediatric wards. This is usually for children with special medical needs, and on an unplanned basis.

48   There are good examples of jointly-funded short break services for children with **complex needs** in community settings. Nursing staff work alongside organisations providing social care to meet healthcare needs. This prevents using hospitals unnecessarily.

An example of good practice

Highland health board and Highland social work department jointly-fund the Orchard. This is a residential respite service for children and young people with **complex needs**.

49   What is clear is that the chances of being able to get a break varies significantly across the country and there is still a need for more short breaks for both children and adults. While there is an overall shortfall in what is being provided, it is difficult to work out accurately by how much.

An example of good practice

Aberlour Child Care Trust has a respite care residential service for children in the Borders. Other health needs are met by nursing staff from Borders General Hospital paediatric services. Nursing staff are seconded to work alongside social care staff to make sure they meet children's health needs to prevent them going into hospital.

50   The Scottish Executive launched their Strategy for Carers in Scotland in November 1999. It means local authorities need to spend £10 million of their grant-aided spending for 2000-01 on services for carers (including short breaks), £5 million from their present budgets and a further £5 million from the new resources made available in that year. The Scottish Executive wants to formally involve carers' organisations in considering how these resources should be used. This should lead to a real increase in short breaks. Ministers have made it clear they will consider targeting extra resources if it does not. The Scottish Executive will monitor the outcome of the carers' strategy for people with learning disabilities. However, we were so struck by the pressure on families of people with learning disabilities that we believe there will be a need for further investment. A carer told us:

'Caring is demanding and stressful. We need to feel that we are doing a good job. If there is no support for us, we cannot continue to care.'

A structured approach to planning short breaks

51   We see two main themes coming from the review.

- Families want more breaks and want flexible planned breaks at home and elsewhere.
- Parents want a wider range of social and leisure experiences for their families through better access to **mainstream** play and out-of-school activities, child care services, education and leisure facilities.

52   Short breaks need to be flexible and meet the individual needs of children, adults and those with more **complex needs**. Carers of people with learning disabilities need better support if they are to continue to care and avoid caring crises.

An example of good practice

The National Children's Home – Gilmerton Road project in Edinburgh provides respite care, residential and peripatetic services for children and young people who have learning disabilities and emotional and behavioural difficulties.

53   Good arrangements for short breaks and shared care depend on simple procedures. Whether the short break is provided by another family or by an agency, the worker's role is to help with this process. They need to be as flexible as possible.

54   No child or adult should have a short break in a hospital setting unless they are in need of specialist treatment or assessment that cannot reasonably be provided elsewhere.

Recommendation 19   Health Boards should contribute funding and resources (for example, training for residential and family carers) to developing community-based short breaks alongside local authorities. Local authorities will also be able to bid for any 'change funds' which may be made available for further developing short breaks for people with learning disabilities.

Recommendation 20   The Scottish Executive and local authorities should review their guidance and procedures to make sure that local authorities and health boards can arrange their short break and shared care arrangements for children and adults flexibly and with as little bureaucracy as possible.

Public attitudes

55   We paid for research to find out about public attitudes to learning disabilities by surveying over 1,000 adults in Scotland[63]. Most felt that people with learning disabilities are just like other people and have the right to live, learn and work alongside everybody else. Most thought that people with learning disabilities should not live in hospitals. However, the survey also showed that ordinary people do not know very much about learning disabilities and that this may lead to prejudice and confusion.

56   Giving people with learning disabilities a more positive profile in communities and schools is an important step on the way to changing public attitudes. Research shows that effective strategies for changing public attitudes work best when there is a positive personal contact for example, helping a customer with learning disabilities. Sharing relevant personal information such as encouraging people with learning disabilities to talk about themselves and their lives, also works well.

57   Regrettably, bullying and harassment are all too often part of the life of people with learning disabilities. A recent report says that 65% of people who took part had experienced bullying; 38% of them said it happened regularly[64]. Many of those responsible were children and young adults. Most victims felt uncomfortable about reporting incidents. If they did, it was effective in 38% of cases.

58   It seems obvious that the general public needs to have a better understanding of people with learning disabilities. That need is greatest among children and young adults. The Scottish Executive has already a programme against bullying in schools.

Recommendation 21   There should be a long-term programme to promote public awareness about learning disabilities and including people with disabilities in the community. This should include programmes from the earliest years of education. The new centre for learning disability could be responsible for taking this forward.

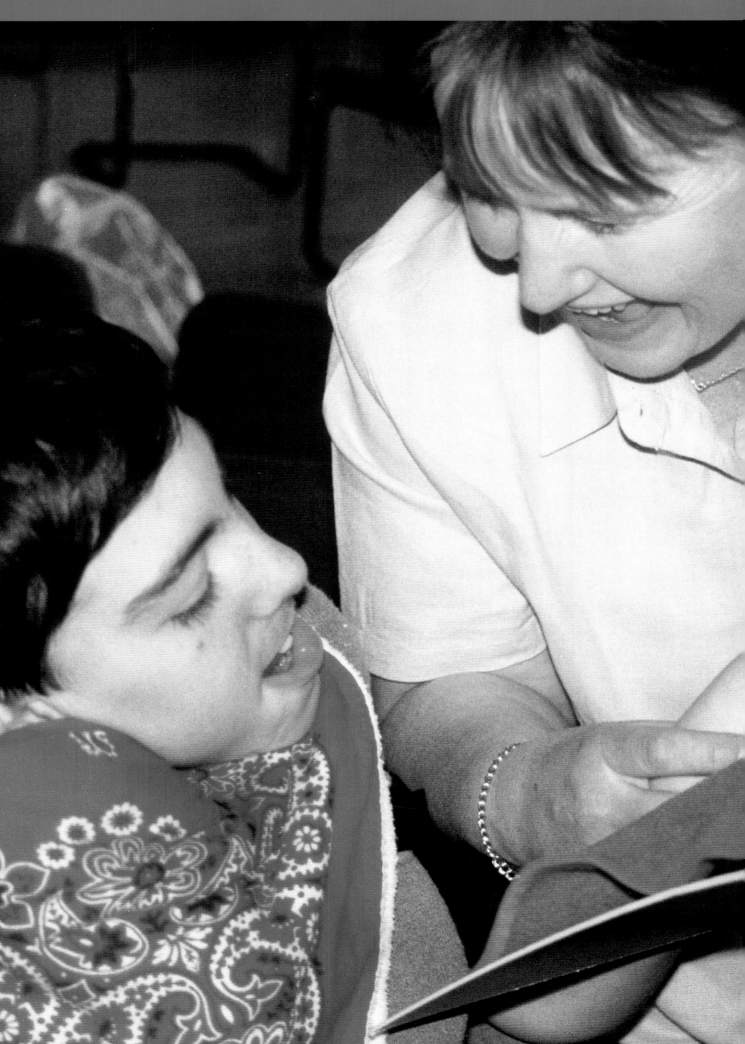

6 Working well together

1   Good partnerships between all the people, agencies and professionals involved in supporting people with learning disabilities are essential if they are to get the services they need when they need them. This chapter focuses on:

- the importance of professionals working closely with people with learning disabilities, their families, friends and relatives and building on these natural forms of support;
- the need for professionals to work together better so that the vulnerability and risk experienced by many people with learning disabilities in different areas of their lives is managed better; and
- professionals working better together to help people through the many different stages in their lives, as they develop and their needs change.

At the end of this chapter, we consider:

- the role of primary and general healthcare;
- people with learning disabilities who have mental health problems;
- people with **challenging behaviour**;
- people with learning disabilities in the criminal justice system; and
- people with profound and multiple learning disabilities.

Where we are now

2   We all use family, friends and people in the community to help us in our daily lives. People with learning disabilities are no different and the contribution made by this natural form of support is not only significant in itself, but also important for other services to recognise and build on. Yet this does not tend to be the starting point of planning and delivering services. As we highlight earlier there are many information gaps, but the greatest are to do with carers and family support.

3   People with learning disabilities are vulnerable. They suffer high levels of both physical and sexual abuse[65]. People with learning disabilities are often the victims of crime, many of which are not reported or followed up

through the criminal justice system[66]. The Mental Welfare Commission for Scotland drew attention to the lack of proper assessment and co-ordination of care in relation to one vulnerable person with a learning disability in their 1998/9 Annual Report[67]. We look at this case in more detail below.

4   Present arrangements for assessing, planning and support are not working as well as they could. Professionals do not work as well as they should with the person with learning disabilities or their family. Nor do they always work well with each other. People are assessed by many different agencies and professionals for different and limited purposes, yet too often no clear plan of action is made as a result. For instance, it is not uncommon for people to find themselves in contact with more than one occupational therapist either from:

- a medical service;
- a learning disability service; or
- social work services.

5   We were also told that information about good practice between professionals working with people with learning disabilities is not shared enough. This also applies to those in other specialist services, such as for people with mental health problems, older people and so on.

6   There is general agreement that the everyday health needs of people with learning disabilities too often go unrecognised and untreated. Health promotion and health screening services, hearing and sight tests which are accessible to most of the population are under-used by people with learning disabilities[68]. Everyday health needs are the responsibility of GPs and the primary care team. However, it has been reported that two-thirds of people with learning disabilities need more health support than primary care can provide[69]. Specialised health needs often need referring on to other specialists, for example, specialist consultants, professionals allied to medicine and community learning disability teams. For many young people with **complex needs** the supports they need will be lifelong.

7   People in our user and carer survey were concerned that healthcare professionals did not spend enough time in assessing the health needs of the person. Some parents believed that healthcare professionals did not know enough about learning disabilities because they had not been given enough

training. There is evidence that when professionals train together they develop a better understanding of each other's roles.

8   Planning for the different stages in people's lives is also neglected. In our user and carer survey most families felt that assessments do not take account of their children's future needs, such as moving from:

- school to further education or resource centres;
- education to employment;
- hospital to community placements;
- services for children to those for adults or older people.

Even more importantly, they reported a lack of co-ordinated planning for the time when they would no longer be there.

An example of good practice

PAMIS (Profound and Multiple Impairment Service) runs training workshops for parents and carers on future planning, legal, financial and housing issues.

9   Caring for a person with a learning disability can be a worthwhile and rewarding experience for many family carers. However it can also place a strain on their emotional well-being, health, finances and relationships. Studies of the psychological well-being of mothers caring for disabled children show higher levels of anxiety and depression compared to women in general. These levels are significantly higher for those caring for children who have other learning disabilities and **complex needs**[70]. During the review carers highlighted the fact that the issues they face are a *constant* feature of their lives. The opportunities they want to take and the problems they try to overcome are not simply present when they get professional attention.

10   Too often at the moment services for people with learning disabilities do not take a wide enough view. Services need to be much more centred on the experience of the people involved, both to meet their needs and to be effective. A system that arranges a tenancy for a person with a learning disability, but leaves them lonely with nothing to do is based around the

service, and does not put the person first. A professional who does not take account of parents' views when they have provided care for 25 years is not setting the service in the full context of the lives of those involved.

11   Effective partnerships between all the people and professionals involved in supporting people with learning disabilities depend on developing **natural supports** in the community such as family and friends *and* using specialist knowledge and expertise to build and maintain long-term benefits. Professionals and others do best when they arrange the service they offer by taking account of the lives of the people they are trying to help.

12   By building natural links and relationships into assessment and planning and developing care, agencies will use their resources more effectively and get better results for people.

Vulnerability and risk

13   Risk features in several different areas of life for people with learning disabilities. Their general vulnerability makes them a target for abuse. They may be exposed to risks in leading a full life. Sometimes, there are risks for them and others, for instance, around taking and giving medicines. These risks need to be assessed and managed. They should never be an excuse for not taking action or taking inappropriate action which does not take account of what users and carers want and need to lead as full a life as possible.

14   We have already said that, wherever they live, people with learning disabilities sometimes experience high levels of sexual or physical abuse and are more likely to be victims of crime. The Mental Welfare Commission's 1998/9 Annual Report highlights a particular case of someone with a mild to moderate learning disability who lived a chaotic life after her mother died, being exploited by several people. She was seriously assaulted and continued to be vulnerable even when it was obvious to professionals that her learning disability was affecting her judgement.

15   The inquiry decided that there had not been enough supervision and protection during the period under review and that the assessment of risk was not dealt with well enough in case discussions. It is very important that social work departments understand when it is appropriate to resort to using compulsory powers to protect through **guardianship**.

16   The Mental Welfare Commission's Report made some far-reaching recommendations including that the **Care Programme Approach** should be used for people with learning disabilities who have **complex needs**. We agree with this recommendation. We have responded to some of their other recommendations here and elsewhere as they are relevant to our concerns to strengthen assessment and planning care. They are also relevant to improving the knowledge and skills of the various professionals who work with people with learning disabilities.

17   Many of those we interviewed during the review told us that too much time, money and energy was spent on over-protecting people with learning disabilities. As ordinary citizens we can make many decisions about the risks we take in our lives. We may choose to go rock-climbing, knowing that injury is possible, but the sense of achievement makes it worthwhile. People with learning disabilities need support to achieve their personal goals. This should not mean putting them at risk but it also does not mean over-protecting them. For this to be possible, users, carers, support staff and managers need to be clear about what risks are acceptable. The Scottish Executive has recently issued guidance for nurses, health visitors and midwives on protecting vulnerable people[71]. Some local authorities already have a policy and provide staff training on assessing and managing risk. This should be the case for all.

Recommendation 22   The Scottish Executive's National Care Standards Committee is currently developing standards for residential and nursing care homes for all care groups including people with learning disabilities. These standards should look clearly at assessing and managing risk in working with vulnerable people.

Recommendation 23   All local authorities in association with health boards, NHS trusts and other agencies should develop policies and guidelines on protecting vulnerable adults. Social work departments should review their procedures on guardianship to include making a formal assessment of risk a normal part of deciding whether an application should be made. Local authorities and health boards should use the Care Programme Approach for people with learning disabilities who have complex needs whether these needs are caused by disability or vulnerability.

Handling transitions better

18   The needs of many people with learning disabilities are lifelong and change as they get older. It is very important that services recognise this and work together to make sure moving from one stage of a person's life to another is planned for and managed as smoothly as possible. This section suggests ways in which agencies might manage this better. It links back to our proposal for personal life plans.

Early years

19   When parents are told that their newborn baby (or child) has a condition which includes learning disabilities, their lives are changed for ever. Their child may still be the greatest source of joy and inspiration and bring pleasure and pride to them, their family and friends. However, their world will not be as it was. They may face many challenges, some of which may frustrate or exhaust them.

20   If a child is born with a learning disability or fails to reach expected early developmental milestones families need:

- information, practical help and emotional support from knowledgeable professionals;
- access to ongoing advice, local child care, paediatric and child health services which can meet their child's needs;
- therapy services included with ordinary children's services;
- programmes which teach parents and carers in nurseries, schools and respite settings how best to help each child develop; and
- early information, advice and options for pre-school and primary education.

School years

'The most important rights of children and young people with Special Educational Needs (SEN) are the right to an appropriate education and the right to be fully integrated into the community to which they belong when they are adults. Inclusion in ordinary schools or, segregation into special classes or schools, is only defensible if it facilitates these two rights' (Hornby)[72].

21   The Scottish Executive's current policy aims to increase **social inclusion** but accepts a need for special schools. Every child should have full-time education that meets their needs, and support to make the most of the learning opportunities available. The new Education Bill before Parliament plans to bring forward a provision at the committee stage of the Bill to the effect that "It shall be presumed that, where under the 1980 Act an education authority are to provide school education for any child of school age, such education shall be provided in a school other than a special school." Local authorities have particular responsibilities to assess and support children with special educational needs. This includes children with learning disabilities.

22   Special schools provide for a smaller number of children whose needs are too great for most ordinary schools to meet, such as those with **profound** and **multiple disabilities**. Some profoundly disabled children manage well in **mainstream** classrooms with a lot of support.   The Scottish Executive has issued guidance for staff working with children in educational settings on providing intimate care for children and young people with disabilities[73]. The most important consideration is that the education should be good-quality and meet the child's needs, not least their wish to be included and have friends.

23   We share the view of the Riddell Advisory Committee on Education Provision for Children with Severe or Low Incidence Disabilities that, in future, a higher number of children with severe low-incidence disabilities will be included in **mainstream** schools close to home. However, they will need specialist services to make sure that their education, health and social needs are met[74]. Specialist and **mainstream** services need to work together to achieve these aims. Setting up a National Special Educational Needs Advisory Forum, to be chaired by the Deputy Minister for Education, Culture and Sport will give the Scottish Executive a way of monitoring developments in this area.

24   Whatever form of provision is most suited to a child's needs, it should form part of the family's wider network of support so that the family experiences a 'seamless' service. A number of people told us there is little continuity of service or staff, and relevant information is not exchanged when children move from early years to primary and then secondary education.

Future Needs Assessment

25   Future Needs Assessment and putting it in place is particularly important to young people with learning disabilities. When a child has a **Record of**

Needs and reaches 14, education authorities must get ready to carry out a future needs assessment (FNA). This, and the action that follows from it, is particularly important to young people with learning disabilities. This should consider whether the child would benefit from school education after he or she has reached the statutory school leaving age (16), whether the Record should be continued throughout the period the young person is still at school and what provision is needed after school. The Record must be discontinued when the young person stops receiving school education or reaches his or her eighteenth birthday. Social work services have a duty to assess whether a recorded child is disabled and, if so, to carry out an assessment of the young person's need for social care services.

26   There are several difficulties with the current arrangements:

- the child and family may have had little contact with social work services before the FNA;
- the social work contribution to the FNA is usually from children's services, which may have limited knowledge of **post school education**, and welfare services available to young adults;
- at the point of handover to community care services for adults there may be a need for a further assessment;
- there is no legal duty on agencies to put the FNA into practice as there is with the **Record of Needs**;
- healthcare needs are not always considered;
- social work services rarely offer options that would include committing financial resources two to five years ahead;
- there is a focus on existing services, and access to day care, rather than needs-led person-centred planning;
- education authorities have no responsibility for putting the FNA into practice after the child has left school; and
- putting the FNA into practice often proves difficult as it relies on resources provided by other agencies.

27   We believe it is necessary to introduce a new duty for local authorities to identify a responsible person (who could be the local area co-ordinator) to advise and help the person with learning disabilities and their family put the FNA into practice (unless they say otherwise).

Recommendation 24   The Scottish Executive should consider introducing a new duty on local authorities to identify a responsible person to advise and help the person with learning disabilities and their family put the FNA into practice.

28   On leaving school young adults and their families may no longer have access to the same short break services, with which they are familiar and comfortable. And the educational opportunities to learn and develop which they had at school may not be available. Local authorities are responsible for meeting these needs, and for co-ordinating the contribution of other partners (including further education college boards of management). GPs, paediatric, learning disability and physical disability services should agree arrangements for people moving from child to adult services to make sure people have appropriate continuity in the healthcare they receive.

29   Making an early start on changing the existing patterns of service is important. We realise that a number of authorities have taken policy decisions not to place any future school leavers in existing day centres. We believe that local authorities throughout Scotland should consider this approach.

Adulthood

30   Needs change over time and as people take up new opportunities they may blossom and look for more. A person leaving hospital may be happy in a small group setting at first but eventually want a home of their own. A person leaving school may want some further education but eventually want a job. Some people with learning disabilities will develop long-term relationships and a number will want to get married. Professionals need to be ready to respond to changing needs as people develop.

31   Professionals and services need to recognise that adolescents and adults with learning disabilities have sexual rights and needs, while at the same time making sure those who may be vulnerable to abuse are protected. The current review of the Mental Health Act is considering how best to protect people with learning disabilities. At present, it is an offence for a man to 'knowingly have sexual intercourse with a woman if she is suffering from a state of arrested or incomplete development of mind which includes significant impairment of intelligence or social functioning'[75]. While this

provides appropriate protection for some people, there are also concerns that people's right to express their sexuality is denied by some services. Some agencies in Scotland have developed policies on sexuality and relationships for people with learning disabilities and we agree with this.

We think local joint policies should include:

- appropriate and accessible information;
- advice and guidance to staff supported by appropriate training;
- access to family planning services; and
- an assessment of risk and the need for protection.

32   Some people with learning disabilities may choose to be parents. As with other parents, they will need a range of support and other help from their families and other agencies. Like other people, parents with learning disabilities can benefit from training and support in developing parenting skills. Some areas offer extra support which is helpful to them and their children[76].

An example of good practice

Grampian primary care trust employ a specialist health visitor to support parents who have learning disabilities. This project involves clinical psychologists, social workers and primary care staff working together.

33   Local authorities and NHS trusts should make sure that the needs of parents with learning disabilities and their children are identified and met.

Growing older

34   Improvements in health and social care mean that people with learning disabilities can now expect to live longer. While people with **complex needs** and people with Down's syndrome still have a reduced life expectancy, people with milder learning disabilities now have a life expectancy similar to other adults in the general population[77]. Older people with learning disabilities should not be seen as different from older people generally. Services need to reflect all the needs of older people and the extra needs of those with

learning disabilities. A recent review of the literature identifies large areas of need which have not been met amongst older people with learning disabilities and services are often not aware of them[78].

35   Local authorities and health services need to make sure that older people with learning disabilities have the same access to health and social care support as older people generally. They should make sure there are links with **mainstream** services for older people and those with dementia to identify the most appropriate services to provide. Specialist knowledge is important here as elsewhere and health boards and local authorities should make sure that there are local professionals who have appropriate expertise to make sure dementia is diagnosed early on. Health services should promote the health and well being of older people with learning disabilities.

36   Older people with learning disabilities and people with dementia will need appropriate day services and recreational opportunities with appropriate links to the **mainstream** services for older people. Health boards, NHS trusts and social work departments should make sure that care staff and support workers have the training they need to meet the needs of older people and those with dementia.

Recommendation 25   Health boards and local authorities should make sure that local professionals are trained to look out for early signs of dementia and so can provide assessment and appropriate responses and services.

37   Older people with learning disabilities are often cared for by parents who become frail and less able to provide the physical support or care needed. In particular the effect on family carers of caring for children and adults with more **complex needs** has been shown to result in greater health needs, stress, anxiety and depression for the carers[79]. Many parents who are carers find it hard to plan for the future.

38   Professionals should respond to carers' readiness to plan and be sensitive to cultural and ethnic influences that may affect attitudes to family caring. They should consider carers' needs as a very important part of any care package for people with learning disabilities.

An example of good practice

Glasgow primary care NHS trust has developed an ethnic and cultural service for people with learning disabilities by working with the community learning disability services. It provides information and support.

Recommendation 26   Life plans for people with learning disabilities who live with their parents should include plans for a time when parents may no longer be able to provide care.

Bereavement

39   We all experience loss in our lives but for people with learning disabilities the loss of a parent who is a carer may lead to a double crisis. For adults who live with family members, death or increasing frailty of parents may mean having to move home. This can have huge health consequences and the process needs to be handled very carefully[80]. Maintaining as much contact and continuity as possible with friends and others is essential. It is also very important that people with learning disabilities have the time and space to grieve.

The role of primary and general healthcare

40   A general practice with 1500 patients can expect to have 22 to 30 people with mild learning disabilities and up to six people with severe disabilities. People with learning disabilities have a greater need for primary care support but tend to use it less than the general population. People with learning disabilities also may need longer appointments to be able to communicate what they need and this does not always happen. There are some initiatives being developed to help people with learning disabilities communicate more clearly about pain and illness[81].

An example of good practice

SENSE Scotland has developed a health log for people with **complex needs** which is maintained by support providers. The log is used to monitor health issues and help when communicating with health professionals.

41   Health boards should offer regular health checks for all people with learning disabilities. Health professionals should pay particular attention to people with **complex needs**. GPs, paediatricians or specialists in learning disabilities all have a part to play. Primary care NHS trusts need to make sure that there are appropriate links between community learning disability specialists and primary care services. Community learning disability nurses have a particularly important role working between primary care and specialist services. Larger primary care centres might consider choosing a GP with lead responsibility for managing and co-ordinating primary healthcare for people with learning disabilities and their families.

42   The healthcare needs of people with learning disabilities are not always looked at well enough in medical education, including continuing education. Nor are the wider issues about how doctors should best communicate with them. Medical schools and those involved in medical education should examine how good their training is in these respects.

Professions Allied to Medicine (PAMs)

43   **PAMs** work in a number of health, education and social work settings such as health centres, hospitals, schools, nursing homes, day centres and in people's own homes. They can also provide a specialist service as members of community learning disability teams. The main professionals involved in assessing and treating people with learning disabilities include physiotherapists, occupational therapists, speech and language therapists, chiropodists, dieticians and creative therapists such as art, drama and music therapists. Most health boards have specialised paediatric therapists who work with children and families, GP, paediatricians and schools. We were impressed by the quality of service in many areas although staff shortages and an increasing number of referrals of people with **complex needs** has led to difficulties in providing a fair service across the country. We heard of children waiting for up to two years in some areas to see an occupational therapy assistant.

44   While most therapists are employed by the health service some schools employ their own physiotherapists, speech and language therapists and occupational therapists. Local authority social work departments also provide occupational therapy services for people living in the community and there are developing links with health service occupational therapy services in some areas (such as providing equipment). A number of health boards and social work departments have set up joint equipment stores for people using

services and have introduced new arrangements to avoid overlapping assessments. In some areas they are making progress towards a joint occupational therapy service.

45   PAMs have a very significant role to play in services for people with learning disabilities. Many people will be able to use general community and hospital based services for specific treatment. Some people with learning disabilities will need support to use these services. Children and adults with extra and **complex needs** will need ongoing services from a range of **PAMs** linked to community learning disability services. Young people have had difficulty in accessing services when they leave school.

People with learning disabilities and other problems

46   Some people's needs will be lifelong.   Others will have particular needs for services at different times in their lives. More **complex needs** may arise from:

- significant difficulties with communication, moving about or physical or social development;
- the complicated nature of support and services needed to help a person with a learning disability cope with mental health problems, or getting into trouble with the law;
- the difficulties for the person or families, carers and others caused by people who injure themselves, who are aggressive or destructive or who display socially-unacceptable behaviour or other challenges;
- the extraordinary services that may be needed to cope with unusual or rare conditions; and
- specific medical problems such as epilepsy, disruptive or disordered sleeping patterns, problems with eating and poor physical and mental health.

We cover some of the main areas below.

People with mental health problems

47   Local psychiatric services and learning disability services should focus on maintaining positive mental health and providing appropriate assessment and treatment by closely working with social work and primary care colleagues. Some people with learning disabilities who also have mental

health problems are rough sleepers and use night shelters. Ending the need to sleep rough is a key commitment for the Scottish Executive and needs all **mainstream** services to work together better.

48   Health boards should make sure that there are appropriate arrangements for people with learning disabilities who have mental health problems going into hospital. In setting up services, health boards should consider the need to have staff trained in learning disabilities *and* staff trained in mental health. Health boards should make sure that there is agreement on the roles and services provided for children with learning disabilities and mental health problems across paediatric services, learning disability services and child and adolescent mental health services.

49   We need to give special consideration to a small number of people affected by the Mental Health Act. Since 1913 people with learning disabilities have been specifically included with those with mental illness in Scottish Mental Health law. The review of the Mental Health (Scotland) Act 1984[82] is considering whether to continue to include people with learning disabilities within mental health law. In Scotland there are 178 people with learning disabilities **detained** in hospital. 44 are in the State Hospital Carstairs[83]. Most have a mild degree of learning disability. About one-third of people with learning disabilities who are **detained** in hospital have been diagnosed with a mental illness.   However, mental illness is also recognised as a feature for a number of other people who are also **detained**.

People with challenging behaviour

50   The term '**challenging behaviour**' has replaced other terms such as 'difficult' and 'problem' behaviour and is less offensive to many people with learning disabilities. It also emphasises the origins of the behaviour, highlighting the role services need to play rather than blaming the person. The term 'interactional challenge' has recently been suggested as a more appropriate term[84].   This emphasises how the person acts in response to the environment. For the purpose of our review the term '**challenging behaviour**' includes people whose behaviour is very challenging to services, whatever the presumed cause.

51   A small number of people often show **challenging behaviour** frequently, while others display **challenging behaviour** on and off and may only need specialist services at a particular time.

52   Many professionals agree that we should not separate services to people with **challenging behaviour** from general services. However, extra support and specialised services may be necessary. The Department of Health commissioned a report in 1993 which agreed with this view[85].

An example of good practice

The Additional Support Team provides a service to adults with learning disabilities whose support needs are a challenge to existing services. The team's major strength lies in its ability to provide a service that meets the individual's needs in a responsive and flexible way.

53   There should be a range of clinical services and treatments available such as **psychotherapy**, **cognitive behavioural approaches** and **behaviour analysis**[86] [87] [88]. Successful and long-term **therapeutic interventions** will be those that avoid looking at only the specific problem behaviour.

54   Health boards, NHS trusts and social work departments should make sure that care staff and support workers have appropriate training to meet the needs of people with **challenging behaviour**. They also need to consider the support needs of parents and families where children have **challenging behaviour**[89].

55   Joint policies on using restraint[90], and managing aggression, should be in place, supported by training. These policies should also be constantly monitored.

Recommendation 27   Health boards and local authorities should make sure that there is appropriate specialist support such as additional support teams to improve services for people with learning disabilities who have challenging behaviour. The aim of the specialist services should be to support mainstream services and to help people stay in their own homes as far as possible.

People with learning disabilities in the criminal justice system

56   There is some evidence that people with learning disabilities may be over-represented at all levels in the criminal justice system[91, 92]. We do not

have enough information on people with learning disabilities who may be in prison and their needs and vulnerability. People with **autistic spectrum disorders** may also be included in this group. A number of people with learning disabilities who offend may be managed appropriately within the criminal justice system. Using probation and delayed sentencing alongside a therapeutic programme has been shown to be effective at reducing the risk of offending for some people with learning disabilities[93].

57   A small number of people are **detained** under the Mental Health (Scotland) Act because of offending and other 'seriously irresponsible' behaviour. People **detained** because of their learning disabilities and offending or seriously irresponsible behaviour may have a mental illness. The current review of Mental Health law is considering options for this group. We recognise the need for a legal framework for the very small number of people who are a risk to themselves or others.

58   The Mentally Disordered Offenders Strategy[94] identifies the particular needs of people with learning disabilities who show offending behaviour. It also makes appropriate recommendations for providing community services with effective training and support.

59   Health Boards and local authorities should make sure that there are local professionals with expertise in working with offenders with learning disabilities. Services should make sure an appropriate risk assessment is carried out and that treatment and ongoing support are provided as far as possible within the community.

60   Health boards should make sure that secure accommodation is provided for the small number of people who need this. There should be links between secure settings and less-secure forms of accommodation in the community. There should be enough properly-planned aftercare, including access to a range of rehabilitation and training facilities and opportunities. Life plans should include assessing need as part of the planning process for leaving any secure setting. From April 2000 a valid community care assessment is a condition of having support charges met by Housing Benefit if somebody is living in the private rented sector.

Recommendation 28   The Scottish Executive should commission research into the number of people with learning disabilities in prison or in secure accommodation and the arrangements for assessing and providing them with care.   Health boards, local authorities, and police forces should make sure that an appropriate adult scheme is in place to meet the needs of people with learning disabilities who come into contact with the police.

People with profound and multiple learning disabilities

61   The terms '**profound** and **multiple disabilities**' or '**profound** and **complex needs**' have replaced terms such as 'special care', and '**profoundly** handicapped' and are seen as recognising the very specific needs of this group.

62   As well as **profound** learning disability, people will have other physical disabilities and **sensory impairment** or both. Most will also have significant healthcare needs. 66% will have severe epilepsy, most will have difficulties in eating and drinking, and problems with their breathing. As a result, services should meet this range of needs.

63   Information and support for families typically does not include specific information on **profound** and **multiple disabilities**. So, it is important that carers get information on learning disabilities and physical disabilities and **sensory impairment**.

64   Staff providing services to people with **profound** and **multiple disabilities** would benefit from national standards for training in specific procedures. These procedures should include tube-feeding, **continence management**, inserting rectal diazepam and using equipment such as **suction machines**.

An example of good practice

Epilepsy Association of Scotland provides guidelines for training staff in inserting rectal diazepam.

Recommendation 29   Local authorities, by working with health boards and the voluntary sector, should make sure that they look at the extra needs of those with profound and multiple disabilities and those of their carers.   The centre for learning disability should set up a national network of support to local providers offering advice and training on the extra needs of people with profound and multiple disabilities.

7 Summary

1   We recognise that services could do more to help people with learning disabilities to achieve a full life. Our main aim is to help them to be included - in community life, in education, in leisure and recreation, in day opportunities and particularly in employment. They should also have far greater access to **mainstream** services and rely less on specialist services.

2   To achieve these goals means considerable change. We need to improve, reshape and reorganise services, and the public needs to better understand people with learning disabilities and their needs.

3   At the centre of this is a major shift to person-centred and needs-led approaches, which put the individual at the heart of any decisions made. For that to work, people with learning disabilities need better information to make more informed choices, to be supported by an **advocate** if they want, and to have more control over their lives and services.

4   We want to improve systems. The local area co-ordinators will:

- co-ordinate and arrange support and services;
- act as a voice for people with learning disabilities;
- have a budget to buy new, local and cost-effective services.

These co-ordinators will replace care managers, and care management, which is not performing well enough. And, to plan for the medium and longer terms, every person who wants to have one should have a 'personal life plan'.

5   The role of services also needs to change. We want them to focus now on including people with learning disabilities in the community, supporting their personal development and their carers. The balance of care needs to shift. People want to have their own homes in the community. Very few people should have hospital as their home, and other forms of shared living should reduce. Day services have to modernise and focus more on education, employment and personal fulfilment. We need more support for carers. This means more flexible and fresh ideas for short breaks.

6   People with learning disabilities, their carers and providers need someone to act for them and promote a better general understanding of learning disabilities. The Scottish centre for learning disability would do this by being a centre of excellence, providing leadership to agencies in the field and advice in general.

7   To serve people with learning disabilities better, agencies need to be much clearer about their roles and the opportunities for working with others (particularly for people with extra and **complex needs**). We need effective partnerships between agencies, between professionals, and between users, carers and professionals.

8   We need to add to all these steps by helping the public generally to be more aware and understanding of learning disabilities. We believe our on-going programme of awareness will achieve this.

9   The scale of change we are looking for from the review has never been seen before in learning disability services in Scotland. We cannot achieve this using current resources. But spending on learning disability services is already considerable, and making better use of that is an essential starting point. A 'change fund' to help local authorities deliver the new agenda seems essential.

10   Finally, we need to monitor practice and progress to make sure that the changes we have mentioned in this review take place and are developed and maintained. The proposed centre and the new Commission will have important roles in making sure that this happens. The real test will be that the lives of people with learning disabilities and their carers are made richer and fuller as a result of the changes proposed here.

11   Users and carers have waited a long time for this review. They have told us very clearly and consistently what they want and need to lead lives which are as fulfilling as possible. What they are asking for is no more than all of us want for ourselves and our children. We do not think that is asking too much.

Appendix 1 List of recommendations

Recommendation 1   Each local authority or group of authorities and health boards should draw up a 'partnership in practice' agreement by 1 June 2001. . . . .**2-18**

Recommendation 2   Health boards and local authorities should agree to appoint local area co-ordinators for learning disabilities from current resources used for managing care and co-ordinating services. Initial training for putting local area co-ordinators in place will begin in Autumn 2001. . . . .**2-20**

Recommendation 3   Everyone with a learning disability who wants to, should be able to have a 'personal life plan'. (Recommendation 26 builds on this.) **2-22**

Recommendation 4   The Scottish Executive should set up a 'change fund' to help local authorities put in place the recommendations in this review. 2-**24**

Recommendation 5   By 2003, anyone who wants direct payments should be able to have them, and local authorities should be included in the list of possible providers. **2-25**

Recommendation 6   The Scottish Executive should set up a new Scottish centre for learning disability. This would offer advice, training and support to agencies, professionals, people with **2-27**

Recommendation 7   The Scottish Society for Autism by working with the National Autistic Society and health boards and local authorities should develop a national network for people with an autistic spectrum disorder. **2-29**

Recommendation 8   The Scottish Accessible Information Forum should consult local authorities, health boards and users and carers on how best to provide joint, one-stop, free and accessible local information services for people with learning disabilities, their families and carers. Information must also be available in community languages. **3-33**

Recommendation 9   The first PIP agreements should set out how local authorities, health boards and primary care trusts will set up and maintain local registers. **3-35**

Recommendation 10   The Scottish Executive's review of the effectiveness of funding speech and language therapy for children should also include services for adults. **3-36**

Recommendation 11   The Scottish Executive should continue to encourage the development of local independent advocacy services. **3-37**

Recommendation 12   Health boards should make sure they have plans now for closing all remaining long-stay hospitals for people with learning disabilities by 2005. . . . .**4-46**

Recommendation 13   Health boards should aim to reduce their assessment and treatment places specifically for people with learning disabilities to four for every 100,000 population across the country as a whole. Health boards should plan for appropriate community services to avoid in-patient assessments and treatment. **4-47**

Recommendation 14   Health Boards with sites remaining after 2002 should develop, with their partners, other services in the community as a priority and set aside resources to meet these costs. This will feature in planning guidance and the boards' performance management arrangements. **4-48**

Recommendation 15   Local authorities and health boards, should both examine what they provide and develop more modern, flexible and responsive services which support people in the community through employment, lifelong learning and getting them involved socially. Day healthcare services for people with learning disabilities should be mixed with those in the community. **5-56**

Recommendation 16   Local authorities need to give much greater priority to developing a range of employment opportunities for people with learning disabilities. And, with health boards those authorities should lead by example in employing more people with learning disabilities. **5-60**

Recommendation 17   The Scottish Executive should consider raising, with the Department of Social Security specific areas of concern related to benefits and support for people with learning disabilities. **5-63**

Recommendation 18   Local authorities should review their local transport services, to make sure that people with learning disabilities can use public services wherever possible. **5-64**

Recommendation 19   Health Boards should contribute funding and resources (for example, training for residential and family carers) to developing community based short breaks alongside local authorities. Local authorities will also be able to bid for any 'change funds' which may be made available for further developing short breaks for people with learning disabilities. **5-69**

Recommendation 20   The Scottish Executive and local authorities should review their guidance and procedures to make sure that local authorities and health boards can arrange their short break and shared care arrangements for children and adults flexibly and with as little bureaucracy as possible. . . .**5-69**

Recommendation 21   There should be a long-term programme to promote public awareness about learning disabilities and including people with disabilities in the community. This should include programmes from the earliest years of education. The new centre for learning disability could be responsible for taking this forward. **5-70**

Recommendation 22   The Scottish Executive's National Care Standards Committee is currently developing standards for residential and nursing care homes for all care groups including people with learning disabilities. These standards should look clearly at assessing and managing risk in working with vulnerable people. **6-76**

Recommendation 23   All local authorities in association with health boards, NHS trusts and other agencies should develop policies and guidelines on protecting vulnerable adults. Social work departments should review their procedures on guardianship to include making a formal assessment of risk a normal part of deciding whether an application should be made. Local authorities and health boards should use the Care Programme Approach for people with learning disabilities who have complex needs whether these needs are caused by disability or vulnerability. **6-76**

Recommendation 24   The Scottish Executive should consider introducing a new duty on local authorities to identify a responsible person to advise and help the person with learning disabilities and their family put the FNA into practice. **6-80**

Recommendation 25   Health boards and local authorities should make sure that local professionals are trained to look out for early signs of dementia and so can provide assessment and appropriate responses and services. **6-83**

Recommendation 26   Life plans for people with learning disabilities who live with their parents should include plans for a time when parents may no longer be able to provide care. . . . . **.6-83**

Recommendation 27   Health boards and local authorities should make sure that there is appropriate specialist support such as additional support teams to improve services for people with learning disabilities who have challenging behaviour. The aim of the specialist services should be to support mainstream services and to help people stay in their own homes as far as possible. . . . . **.6-89**

Recommendation 28   The Scottish Executive should commission research into the number of people with learning disabilities in prison or in secure accommodation and the arrangements for assessing and providing them with care.   Health boards, local authorities, and police forces should make sure that an appropriate adult scheme is in place to meet the needs of people with learning disabilities who come into contact with the police. . . . . **.6-90**

Recommendation 29   Local authorities, by working with health boards and the voluntary sector, should make sure that they look at the extra needs of those with profound and multiple disabilities and those of their carers. The centre for learning disability should set up a national network of support to local providers offering advice and training on the extra needs of people with profound and multiple disabilities. . . . . **.6-91**

Appendix 2 National implementation plan

May 2000	Launch the report for consultation
June 2000	Issue specification and invite bids for setting up the Scottish centre for learning disabilities
October 2000	Receive responses
March 2001	National Care Standards for people with learning disabilities in care homes completed
March 2001	Standards for day and **domiciliary services** completed
April 2001	'Change fund' for developing local services launched
2001	Scottish Commission for the Regulation of Care set up
2001	Scottish Social Services Council set up
June 2001	First 'partnership in practice' agreements to Scottish Executive
Spring 2001	Award the contract for setting up the centre for learning disabilities
Autumn 2001	Initial training for putting local area co-ordination in place
Summer 2002	Local area co-ordinators in place
Summer 2002	PIPs fully in place
Spring 2002	All local area co-ordinators electronically linked
2003	Mandatory **direct payments** introduced
2005	All long-stay hospitals closed

Appendix 3 Definitions

During the review, we consulted on how relevant and what purpose a definition in relation to using the term 'learning disability' would be.

We considered the need for an appropriate and meaningful description of the needs of people who may need services or other support because of their learning disabilities. We agreed that there is a need to make sure that people are not disadvantaged as a result of being unable to use appropriate services because of 'definitions' and 'cut-off' points. Likewise, people should not be 'pigeon holed' because of definitions which fail to recognise their ability to develop. It is vital that we identify the needs of people with learning disabilities in a way that allows services to respond appropriately.

In agreeing a definition we considered the following.

- How terminology is used and what it means across different agencies and professional groups. For example, there is currently confusion between terms such as 'learning difficulty', and 'learning disability'.
- What effect using inclusion and exclusion criteria would have.
- The effect of redefining learning disabilities under the mental health legislation.
- The links with recent policy guidance.
- The views of carers, users and other people with an interest.

Terminology

The term 'learning disabilities' is now used throughout the UK particularly in health and social care settings. We are aware that there are some mixed views about this. We can review this (not necessarily the definition) at some point in the future depending on the views of users, carers and others. For interest, the term 'intellectual disability' appears to be replacing 'learning disability' in academic journals and in international organisations.

Inclusion and exclusion criteria

It is generally accepted that we can refer to a person as having a 'learning disability' if the disability has been present before the age of 18. So, we do not consider a person with previous 'normal' functioning, who has a brain injury after age 18 to have a learning disability. Learning disability services may sometimes provide care and support but it is better if appropriate specialised services for people with brain injuries are available. This review does not cover the needs or proposed services for this group.

We also do not include people with specific learning difficulties such as dyslexia in our definition of learning disability.

People with learning disabilities can experience the same range of mental and physical disorders as the general population.   If a person's first diagnosis is learning disability, their needs may best be met by learning disability services and supported by appropriate general and specialist services.   However, we should not deny people with learning disabilities access to other specialised services because they are only seen as people with learning disabilities.

The legal background

The Mental Health (Scotland) Act 1984 is currently being reviewed by the Millan Committee and we believe this will mean the current terminology such as mental handicap, mental impairment and severe mental impairment will change. The proposed Adults with Incapacity Bill[95] has taken on board the current Mental Health Act (Scotland) 1984 definition, although this may be considered again after the Millan Committee's recommendations. Appendix 5 provides a detailed account of the legal framework.

Policy guidance

The Scottish Executive has recently issued some reports of relevance to our review of services[96, 97].

The Riddell report uses a definition of 'severe low incidence disabilities' while the Beattie report refers to the needs of young people 'who require additional support to make the transition to **post school education** and training or employment'.   This can include people with physical disabilities, learning disabilities, mental health problems, low education and attainment and social, emotional and behavioural difficulties.   There is some overlap in relation to the needs of people dealt with by Riddell, Beattie and our own review.

Users' and carers' views

Our analysis of the views of people who wrote to us and our meetings with users and carers identified a range of opinion on using a definition of learning disability and how relevant it is. We have taken account of these views in developing a definition.

The definition

In developing our definition of learning disability, we have taken a flexible approach while making sure that there is a clear definition to help identify need and target resources. An analysis based on needs means that learning disability is not seen as an 'all-or-nothing' condition.

The following definition is based on work done elsewhere[98]:

'A learning disability is a significant, lifelong condition which has three facets:

- reduced ability to understand new or complex information or to learn new skills;
- reduced ability to cope independently; and
- a condition which started before adulthood (before the age of 18) with a lasting effect on the individual's development.'

For the purpose of the review, it includes people with **autistic spectrum disorders**.

People with learning disabilities will need a range of support depending on their needs:

Everyday needs, for example, a place to live, financial security, friendships and opportunities to have a meaningful day.

Extra needs because of their learning disability, for example, help:

- with getting about;
- to use services;
- to understand information; and
- with communication.

Complex needs, for example, support in crisis situations, treatment to improve mental health or to help reduce **challenging behaviour**.

For any one of these needs the level of support necessary may vary.   An individual may need the following.

Occasional and short-term support (intermittent support)

The person will not always need the support or need only short term support during their life. Support may be high or low intensity, simple or complex. It is used for a specific purpose and to provide general support for a person on an 'as-needed' basis. It may also be necessary to support someone in a certain setting.

Time-limited support

This may be high or low intensity and complex. It is limited by time or by some other resource and is typically to support the person through a difficult period or when moving from one stage to another in their lives.

Regular long-term support

This is support involving regular help (for example, daily) in at least some environments and is not limited by time.

Constant and highly-intensive support

This is constant and very intensive support provided across different environments. It could involve medical care to keep the person alive. High-intensive support typically involves more staff and resources.

This approach to a definition should help agencies develop a stronger way of assessing needs and allows for a shared understanding across the different agencies and professional groups.

Appendix 4 The cost of care packages

This appendix compares, in very broad terms, the costs of other care packages and hospital care.

There is very limited information available on the cost of packages and the needs of individuals. The only accurate sources are the studies for the Department of the Environment, Transport and the Regions and the Department of Health we have referred to in chapter 4 of this report. But even these sources acknowledge the small scale of their samples.

The table below offers another pattern of care for the 700 to 800 residents in long-stay hospitals after 2002 (less the 300 to 400 to be held in the NHS) and costs involved.

Figure 3 Other patterns of care

	Number of places	Total revenue cost (see note 1 below)	Net revenue cost (see note 2 below)	Total net revenue cost £million
Adult placements	40	£30,000	£26,000	1.1
Small group homes	130	£50,000	£46,000	6.0
Supported living	200	£59,000	£48,000	9.6
Nursing and residential homes	30	£25,000	£20,000	0.6
				17.3
Hospital places	400	£45,000 (see note 3 below)	£38,000 (see note 4 below)	15.2
Extra net cost	2.1			

Note 1 The total cost of care packages in studies for DETR/DOH referred to in Chapter 4.

Note 2 The cost after taking away benefits income and the cost of **capital**. The result is the on-going running costs of (social and health) care and accommodation.

Note 3 Scottish hospital costs - cost each week of inpatient care.

Note 4 Cost at (3) less assumed allowance for non-recurring, double running costs.

Appendix 5 What will progress look like?

This review aims to change people's lifestyles for the better. Improving the range and quality of services, and the way that agencies work together contribute to that goal. Some benefits should emerge quite quickly, while others will take longer. Our ability to measure progress also varies. Some elements, for example, shifts in the balance between services should be self-evident; but others such as how well people are integrated into the community, are more difficult.

The review expects major changes. Progress should be recognised in the following way.

A Scottish centre for learning disability

- The centre promoting change locally in the way people understand learning disabilities, in the information available to people with learning disabilities and in the range of support available.

A major shift in the balance of care and support services

- All but a small number of long-stay hospital places will go, with specialist healthcare provided in other settings.
- Less formal residential and nursing home care will be provided and many more supported accommodation and adult placements will be used.
- Much less formal day care and many more day opportunities, provided, for example in education, leisure and employment.
- Considerably more people will have real jobs, and others will have a range of employment opportunities.
- More children will be educated in **mainstream** schools.
- Most people with learning disabilities will have access to **mainstream** health, social care, education and employment services.

New and better ways of working

- Local area co-ordinators will be the focal point for securing services and support.

- Jointly commissioned services will be provided for people with **complex needs**.
- People with learning disabilities will have access to independent **advocacy** when they need it.
- **Direct payments** will be available to people who want and can use them.
- Every person who wants one can have a life plan.

A better quality of life

- People with learning disabilities will use independent advocacy and **direct payments** to give them more control of their lives and the services they receive.
- People with learning disabilities will be much more part of the community; living in the community, working in the community, enjoying education, leisure and recreation in the community.
- Measures will be introduced to reduce bullying and harassment of people with learning disabilities.
- People with learning disabilities will enjoy better health and being part of routine screening programmes.

Some of the information to show change will come from existing sources. Some new information will need to be gathered, and because quality of life is such an important element, some specific work (for example, a quality of life survey) may be appropriate.

Appendix 6 The legal background

The main legal requirements for local authorities and health boards to provide social, health, housing, education, employment and services for people with learning disabilities are set out below.

Social Work (Scotland) Act 1968

Section 12

This places a general duty on every local authority to promote social welfare by making advice, guidance and help available on a scale appropriate for their area.

Section 12A

This was added by the National Health Service and Community Care Act 1990 (see section 55). The Social Work (Scotland) Act 1968 was also amended by the Carers (Recognition and Services) Act 1995. This places a duty on the local authority to carry out community care assessments and then decide whether to provide services.

Section 14

This places a general duty on every local authority to provide **domiciliary services** for households where there are people in need. It also gives the power to provide laundry facilities for these households.

Chronically Sick and Disabled Persons

(Scotland) Act 1972

This Act extends sections 1 and 2(1) of the Chronically Sick and Disabled Persons Act 1970 to Scotland.

Section 1 (of the 1970 Act)

This places a duty on every local authority (which has a role under section 12 of the 1968 Act) to know about the numbers of disabled people living in their area and the need to make arrangements for these people. Every local authority should publish general information about the services they provide.

They are also to let disabled people know about relevant services that they know others provide.

Section 2(1) (of the 1970 Act)

This lists the arrangements that can be made to help disabled people. These include:

- practical help for that person in his or her home;

- getting, or helping someone to get a radio, tv, phone, or specialist equipment to be able to use a phone;

- help in using library, recreational or educational facilities;

- providing facilities to, or helping with travel to and from home;

- adaptations to the home;

- holidays; and

- meals.

Section 21

This is the Orange Badge Scheme of parking concessions for disabled and blind people.

Employment and Training Act 1973 (as amended by the Trade Union Reform and Employment Rights Act 1993)

This sets out the duty of the Secretary of State for Scotland to provide relevant services for helping people in education to decide on future employment, and what training may be necessary to fit them for this employment.

Sections 10(1) and 10(2)

These say 'in doing so the Secretary of State shall have regard to the requirements of disabled persons.'

Education (Scotland) Act 1980

Section 1

This places a general duty on education authorities to provide adequate and efficient school education for their area. This must include special educational needs, which covers those with learning difficulties which may arise from a disability.

Section 60(2)

So that education authorities can fulfil their duties in terms of special educational needs, they must find out which children belonging to their area (who are two years old or over but under 16) have obvious, specific or complex special educational needs which need to be reviewed. They must open and keep a **Record of Needs** for any children who, following assessment, have these needs. They also have the power to carry out these functions for children aged between 16 and 18 who are still at school.

Section 65B

This places a duty on the education authority to provide a future needs assessment for any child with special educational needs so that children may benefit from local authority services after leaving school.

Mental Health (Scotland) Act 1984

Sections 2 to 6

These provide for the Mental Welfare Commission for Scotland whose main function is to use their general protective functions for people with mental disorders. This includes those with learning disabilities. The Commission's powers cover people in the community as well as those in hospital or other care settings.

Sections 7 and 8

These give power to local authorities to make arrangements for providing services for people with mental disorders. This includes accommodation for those not in hospital, and, in particular, for after-care services for those who are or have been suffering from mental disorders.

Section 11

This says local authorities must provide training and jobs for people with learning disabilities.

Sections 17-35

These cover care and treatment of patients with mental disorders in hospital. Section 17 sets out the conditions for going into hospital.

Sections 35A to 35K

These sections were introduced by the Mental Health (Patients in the Community) Act 1995. They cover community care orders for people who have left hospital to make sure they receive the services they need while in the community. (However, they do not allow for compulsory treatment in the community).

Sections 36-52

These cover **guardianship** for people with mental disorders if this is appropriate. The **guardian** may be the local authority or an individual.

Sections 60-76

These set out conditions relating to hospital orders and restriction orders for people with mental disorders who have been charged with offences. They also cover transferring prisoners with mental disorders to hospital where appropriate.

Section 94

This covers managing the property of patients who are receiving treatment in hospital for mental disorders (whether or not they are formally held under the Act) and who cannot manage their own affairs.

Part X covers treating mental disorders of patients who are held to whom Part X applies. In particular, it regulates certain treatments (at present electro-convulsive therapy, drug treatment for more than three months, psychosurgery and implanting hormones). Part X1 covers other conditions including offences against people with mental disorders. Part XI contains offences against people with mental disorders (particularly section 106, which regulates sexual relationships with women with learning disabilities). It places a duty on professionals to give information to relatives and carers of patients under **guardianship**. It grants powers to Mental Health Officers and the police to intervene if people with mental disorders are neglected or abused, or need care in a public place.

Disabled Persons (Services, Consultation and Representation) Act 1986

Section 4

This places a duty on the local authority to decide whether the needs of a disabled person call for a range of services in line with section 2(1) of the 1970 Act if the disabled person, his or her representative or carer ask for this.

Section 8 (1)

This places a duty on the local authority to take account of the ability of the carer to continue to provide care.

Section 13

This deals with disabled people leaving special education in Scotland. Under this section local authorities have a duty to assess the needs of disabled children in relation to providing services 'in accordance with the welfare enactments, and for that assessment to be carried out'.

Housing (Scotland) Act 1987

Section 1

This places a duty on local authorities to consider the housing needs of their area, and in doing so, take account of the needs of chronically sick or disabled people.

Section 236

This gives local authorities the power to pay improvement grants to, amongst others, disabled occupants.

National Health Service and Community Care Act 1990

Section 47 (2)

This says that if, during an assessment of need, a person appears to be disabled, the local authority will move automatically to make a decision on services.

Section 55

This added a new section 12A into the 1968 Act under which the local authority would carry out assessments of needs and would then decide whether these needs call for services.

Enterprise and New Towns Act 1990 (as amended by the Trade Unions Reform and Employment Rights Act 1993)

Section 2(3)

This deals with Training for Work. It says that Scottish Enterprise and Highlands and Islands Enterprise must each make appropriate arrangements for helping people to train so that they may get and keep suitable jobs.

Section 2(4)

This says that the above should include arrangements for encouraging more opportunities for (and types of) employment and training that are available to disabled people.

Further and Higher Education (Scotland) Act 1992

Section 1

This says the Secretary of State has a duty to "secure adequate and efficient provision of further education in Scotland". Further education which this duty applies to is described in the Act as amended by Schedule 5, paragraph 8, of the Education (Scotland) Act 1996. In carrying out his duty, the Secretary of State "shall have regard to the requirements of persons over school age who have learning difficulties". The term learning difficulties is used in the Act in its broad sense to include difficulties in learning and barriers to learning.

Carers (Recognition and Services) Act 1995

Section 2 (1)

This changes section 12A of the 1968 Act to make an independent assessment of carers' needs when they ask for this.   However, this only applies if the care they offer is substantial and regular.

Disability Discrimination Act 1995

Section 19

This makes it illegal for anyone providing services to discriminate against a disabled person in relation to access, for example, how information is used and how communication is used.

Part V

This is a matter for the Westminster Parliament and covers regulations to set minimum conditions for providing access for disabled people to public transport vehicles. Rail Vehicle Accessibility Regulations came into force on 1 January 1999. Regulations on access to buses, coaches and taxis are at various stages of being prepared.

The Children (Scotland) Act 1995

Section 22

This places a duty on local authorities to protect and promote the welfare of children in need in their area.

Section 23

This introduces a new legal framework for assessment, services, and support to children with disabilities, children affected by disabilities and their families. The principle behind this is that services are designed to reduce the negative effect of the child's disability and improve the child's opportunity to lead as normal a life as possible.

Section 24

In carrying out an assessment to decide on the needs of a disabled child the local authority must assess a carer's ability to provide, and to continue to provide, care for that child.

Criminal Procedure (Scotland) Act 1995

Sections 52 to 63

These cover putting people accused of offences in hospital if they have mental disorders.

Sections 60 to 76 of the 1984 Act set out the conditions relating to hospital orders and restriction orders for people with mental disorders who have been charged with offences. They also cover transferring prisoners with mental disorders to hospitals where appropriate.

Direct Payments Act 1996

This amends the Social Work (Scotland) Act 1968, section 12B and section 12C.

The Adults With Incapacity (Scotland) Act

This Act will replace current arrangements for **curators bonis, tutors, tutors dative** and **guardians** appointed under the Mental Health (Scotland) Act 1984. All of these office holders can currently make decisions about either the finances or the welfare of people who do not have the ability legally to make their own decisions.

Prospective Education Bill

This will mean local authorities must provide pre-school education for every three-and four-year-old whose parents want a place. Children with learning disabilities stand to benefit from this duty no less than others.

Appendix 7 Who was involved in the review

Steering Group

The steering group had a responsibility to send Ministers a strategic framework for developing social and healthcare for adults and children with learning disabilities. This had to recognise the importance of access to other relevant services and opportunities.

Members

Mrs Gillian Stewart	Head of Children's and Young People's (Chair) Group
Dr Andrew Fraser	Deputy Chief Medical Officer, Health Department
Mrs Joan Fraser	Education Department (from December 1999)
Mr Richard Grant	Housing Division, Development Department (until June 1999)
Dr Sandra Grant	Chief Executive, Scottish Health Advisory Service
Mr Bob Irvine	Education Department (until September 1999)
Mrs Liz Lewis	Community Care Division, Scottish Executive Health Department
Mr Ian McGhee	Enterprise and Lifelong Learning Department
Mrs Jean MacLellan	Social Work Services Inspectorate
Mr David Meikle	Community Care Implementation Unit
Mr Bill Moore	Housing Division, Development Department (from June 1999)
Mrs Gillian Ottley	Assistant Chief Inspector, Social Services Inspectorate
Mr Angus Skinner	Chief Inspector, Social Work Services Inspectorate
Mrs Jenny McNeill (Secretary)	Community Care Implementation Unit

Plus two representatives from the Users' and Carers' Reference Group, who were nominated to go to each meeting.

Working Group

Members

Mrs Gillian Ottley (Chair)	Assistant Chief Inspector, Social Work Services Inspectorate
Mr Bruce Barnett	NHS Management Executive (until July 1999)
Dr Ken Black	Health Department (until September 1999)
HMI Dr Mike Gibson	Education Department
Mr Tom Leckie	Social Work Services Inspectorate
Mr George McLachlan	NHS Management Executive (from November 1999)
Mrs Jean MacLellan	Social Work Services Inspectorate
Ms Jackie McRae	Social Work Services Inspectorate
Mr David Meikle	Community Care Implementation Unit
Mr John Payne	Community Care Implementation Unit
Dr Pauline Robertson	NHS Management Executive
Mr Robert Samuel	NHS Management Executive
Mr John Templeton	NHS Management Executive
Dr Margaret Whoriskey	Scottish Health Advisory Service
Dr Hugh Whyte	NHS Management Executive
Mrs Jenny McNeill (Secretary)	Community Care Implementation Unit

Stakeholders' Reference Group

Members

Mrs Gillian Ottley (Chair)	Assistant Chief Inspector, Social Work Services Inspectorate
Mr Bruce Anderson	Grampian Health Board
Ms Liz Catterson	Enable
Dr Sally Cheseldine	Lanarkshire Healthcare NHS Trust
Mr John Dalrymple	Support for Ordinary Living
Ms Roseanne Fearon	Lynebank Discharge Programme
Mr Max Gallagher	Real Jobs
Mr Stewart Gibb	Homelink
Professor James Hogg	Dundee University
Dr Ros Lyall	Lothian Primary Care NHS Trust
Mrs Jean MacLellan	Social Work Services Inspectorate
Mr Mike Martin	Capability Scotland
Mr Malcolm Matheson	Key Housing
Mr Colin Meehan	West Dunbartonshire Council
Mr David Meikle	Community Care Implementation Unit
Professor Sheila Riddell	Glasgow University
Mr Pete Ritchie	Scottish Human Services
Mr Denis Rowley	New Directions, City of Edinburgh Council
Mr Chris Taylor	Carr-Gomm
Ms Ann Walker	Camphill Scotland
Dr Iain White	GP, Lossiemouth
Mrs Carole Wilkinson	Falkirk Council
Mrs Jenny McNeill (Secretary)	Community Care Implementation Unit

Users' and Carers' Reference Group

Members

Mrs Marjorie Arthurs	Partners in Advocacy
Mr David Barraclough	Enable
Mrs Ivy Blair	Shared Care Scotland
Ms Amanda Brown	Barnardo's
Mrs Ursula Corker	Carers National Association
Mr Norman Dunning	Enable
Ms Mary Earl	Enable
Mr Tom Leckie	Social Work Services Inspectorate
Mrs Marion McArdle	PAMIS
Mr James McIntosh	Capability Scotland
Mr James McNab	People First Scotland
Mrs Elizabeth Melville	PAMIS
Mrs Ruth Price	Barnardo's
Mrs Nancy Simpson	Relatives and Carers Group, Gogarburn Hospital
Ms Pam Smith	Scottish Society for Autism
Ms Karen Watchman	Scottish Down's Syndrome Association
Ms Gill West	National Autistic Society
Ms Sheila Williams	Capability Scotland
Mrs Barbara Johnson	Community Care Implementation (Secretary) Unit

Best Practice Task Group

This group was responsible for identifying good practice which provides opportunities for people with learning disabilities to lead fulfilling lives.

Members

Mrs Jean MacLellan (Chair)	Social Work Services Inspectorate
Dr Ken Black	Health Department
Ms Linda Headland	ELCAP
Mr Duncan Macauley	City of Edinburgh Council
Mr Michael McCue	Additional Support Team, Glasgow
Mr John Payne	Community Care Implementation Unit
Mr Dennis Rowley	New Directions, City of Edinburgh Council
Dr Kirsten Stalker	Scotland Human Services
Dr Margaret Whoriskey	Scottish Health Advisory Service

Best Value Task Group

The group assessed whether services make best use of available resources and achieve fairness for people (adults and children) who have learning disabilities.

Members

Mr David Meikle (Chair)	Community Care Implementation Unit
Dr Ken Black	Health Department
Mr John Payne	Community Care Implementation Unit
Mr John Templeton	NHS Management Executive

Children's Services Group

A small group drew upon the expertise of the stakeholders' and users' and carers' groups and involved a wide range of professional and carers' interests by using workshop discussions and consultation and co-ordinated material and issues from other sources.

Members

Ms Jackie McRae, (Chair)	Social Work Services Inspectorate
HMI Dr Mike Gibson	Education Department
Ms Jean Swaffield	NHS Management Executive
Dr Margaret Whoriskey	Scottish Health Advisory Service
Dr David Will	NHS Management Executive

We want to give particular thanks to Partners in Advocacy, Shared Care Scotland, Barnardo's Scotland and Enable for helping us with the workshop on Children's Services.

Complex Needs Task Group

The group was responsible for identifying how services can best meet the needs of those with **complex needs**.

Members

Dr Margaret Whoriskey (Chair)	Scottish Health Advisory Service
Dr Sally Cheseldine	Lanarkshire Healthcare NHS Trust
Mr John Dalrymple	Support for Ordinary Living
Mr Tom Leckie	Social Work Services Inspectorate
Mrs Jean MacLellan	Social Work Services Inspectorate
Ms Marion McArdle	PAMIS
Dr Pauline Robertson	NHS Management Executive
Mr Robert Samuel	NHS Management Executive

Mapping Task Group

The group found out about current services and looked at needs and definitions.

Members

Mr David Meikle (Chair)	Community Care Implementation Unit
Dr Ken Black	Health Department
Mr John Payne	Community Care Implementation Unit
Mr John Templeton	NHS Management Executive
Dr Margaret Whoriskey	Scottish Health Advisory Service

Training Task Group

This group was responsible for identifying staff development needs.

Members

Mrs Jean MacLellan (Chair)	Social Work Services Inspectorate
Ms Pat Bagot	Scottish Homes
Dr Ken Black	Health Department
Mr Ian Murray	National Board for Nursing
Mr Brodie Paterson	Stirling University
Mr Ray Pavey	Central Council for Education and Training in Social Work
Ms Kate Pryde	Falkirk Council
Mr Robert Samuel	NHS Management Executive

Appendix 8 Glossary

The following glossary explains the meaning of words that appear in the text.

Advocate/Advocacy	Someone who helps people with learning disabilities to say what it is they need and to make their own decisions. See citizen advocate and self-advocate.
Asperger's syndrome	This is a type of autism (see below) that some people of average intelligence and language ability have. They find it particularly difficult to understand what other people think and this makes it hard for them to communicate and act appropriately.
Autism	This is a lifelong developmental disability that affects the way a person communicates and relates to people around them. People with autism can often have learning disabilities but everyone with the condition shares a difficulty in making sense of the world.
Autistic spectrum disorder	Autism can happen in people with different degrees of learning disability as well as in people of average intelligence, for example, those who have Asperger's syndrome. Because of this wide range, we talk about a spectrum of autistic disorder.
Behaviour analysis	Looking into the cause and effect of behaviour based on what has happened in the past.
Benchmarking	Working out how good a service is by comparing it to another service that has set a high standard.

Bridging finance	Money that the Scottish Executive gives to health boards to help them set up new services in the community while they are still paying for running hospitals.
Brokerage service	Somewhere people with learning disabilities can go to get independent help in deciding on and buying the services they need.
Capital	Money spent on buying things that will last longer than a year, for example, land, buildings, equipment.
Care Programme Approach	A way of making sure that all those with serious mental health problems and complex needs have an assessment and care plan that all the different professionals agree on (for example, social workers and doctors). This is checked regularly to see how well the person is doing.
Challenging behaviour	A term used to describe when someone is acting in a way that might do themselves or others harm. People who care for these people are 'challenged' to stop the harm. That is why we call it 'challenging behaviour'.
Citizen advocate	An 'unpaid' volunteer who is independent of the services, a person with learning disabilities receives. This advocate represents the needs of the person and supports them to make sure they get their rights.
Clinical engineer	Someone who helps to improve mobility in a variety of ways including providing wheelchairs.
Cognitive behavioural approaches	Ways of understanding and changing what people do and feel – mostly used by psychologists and psychiatrists.

Commissioning	Deciding what services are needed and then getting someone to provide these by signing a contract.
Complex needs	This describes the needs a person has over and above their learning disability. For example, extra physical or mental health problems, challenging behaviour or offending behaviour.
Continence management	Trying to help people who have problems with bladder and bowel control.
Continuing care	Nursing or medical help or both of a level that cannot be provided in a care or nursing home.
Curator bonis	A person appointed by the court to manage the whole of another person's property and money.
Detained patient	Someone who is made to stay in hospital under a section of the Mental Health (Scotland) Act 1984 or the Criminal Procedure (Scotland) Act 1995.
Direct payments	Local authorities giving people money to buy their own social care services so that they have more say in how their needs are met.
Domiciliary services	Care services provided to a person in their own home.
Dual diagnosis	Where someone has both a learning disability and mental health problems.
Early onset dementia	A term used to describe people who get dementia at an earlier age than might be expected. This leads to a variety of

problems, including difficulties in remembering, making decisions, and learning new skills. These difficulties get worse as time passes.

Guardian/guardianship

A guardian for a child is someone appointed by a parent, or, where necessary, the sheriff, to take over parents' responsibilities and rights after a parent dies. The guardian's role applies until the child is 18.

A guardian for an adult with a mental disorder is someone appointed by the sheriff who has the power to say where the person lives, gets education and training and also makes sure that doctors can see a person without difficulty.

Learning difficulty

Pre-school and school-age children are usually described as having a learning difficulty rather than a disability when they have special educational needs that need extra or different approaches to the way they are taught.

Mainstream

Generally available to all members of the community.

Managed clinical network

Where healthcare professionals who have an interest in the same area of work share their knowledge and resources to get the best care for patients. A network can be local, regional or national depending on what the work is.

Mapping of services

Finding out what services there are and what they are like.

Mobility

Being able to move from one place to another with or without help.

Multiple disability needs	Where someone needs help with several aspects of life which may include health, education, leisure, financial or housing support and being part of the community.
Natural supports	People who help those with learning disabilities like family and friends and are not paid to do this.
Palliative care	Managing care for someone who is not going to get better.
Peripatetic support staff	Staff who go from place to place to do their work rather than staying in a single centre.
Post school education	The range of education that takes place after school leaving age. It may include further education, community education, higher education, adults going back to school, other kinds of informal education and vocational training.
Prevalence data	A way of working out how many people in a population are likely to have a learning disability.
Professions Allied to Medicine(PAMs)	These are physiotherapy, occupational therapy, chiropody, radiography, dietetics, remedial gymnastics, orthoptics, art, music and drama therapies.
Profound disability needs	A term used to describe someone who has a very severe degree of learning disability which may be associated with **complex needs**. For example, this could include feeding difficulties, physical disabilities or sensory impairment.
Psychotherapy	A psychological treatment based on talking and usually designed to help the person understand what is happening now and how to change it.

Record of Needs

A document opened by an education authority for a child with pronounced, specific or complex educational needs which will lead to regular review and which helps to fund the best way of providing what is needed.

Rectal diazepam

This is a drug inserted up a person's bottom to stop severe epileptic fits.

Revenue

Money spent on day-to-day costs like paying for staff and services.

Self-advocacy

Where people with learning disabilities promote their needs and wishes for themselves.

Sensory impairment

A loss of sight or hearing or both.

Social inclusion

Helping people to feel and be part of the society in which they live. They are 'socially included'.

Suction machine

Equipment used to remove saliva and so on, from the mouth and the back of the throat.

Therapeutic interventions

Giving treatment of any kind – drugs, physical or psychological therapy – to promote a person's well-being.

TUPE

This stands for the Transfer of Undertaking (Protection of Employment Regulations) 1981. It is an agreement about how staff are to be treated if they need to change jobs.

Tutors

The Court of Session can appoint a tutor-at-law or a tutor-dative to an adult with incapacity. Tutors-at-law manage the adult's personal welfare, property and financial affairs. Tutors-dative only have powers over an adult's personal welfare and the court may limit that to particular areas of welfare.

Textual References

1   Department of Health (1995) *The Health of the Nation –A Strategy for People with Learning Disabilities,* London: HMSO.

2   Farmer, R., (1992) *Dimensions in Mental Handicap,* London: Charing Cross and Westminster Medical School.

3   Beange, H, McElduff, A and Baker, W (1995) 'Mental disorders of adults with mental retardation: Population Study', *American Journal of Mental Retardation,* 1995, 595-604.

4   Kerr, N, Fraser W, Felce D (1996) *Primary healthcare for people with a learning disability,* British Journal of Learning Disability, Volume 24, 52-58.

5   Corbett, J (1985) *Mental Retardation: Psychiatric Aspects in Child and Adolescent Psychiatry* Oxford: Blackwell.

6   Cooper, S A (1999) *Elderly compared to younger adults with learning disability: Epidemiology of psychiatric disorders,* British Journal of Psychiatry.

7   McGrother, C W and Thorp, C F (1999) *Planning and Research Information to improve services for people with learning disabilities,* Annual Scientific Meeting of the Faculty of Public Health Medicine, Glasgow.

8   Information and Statistics Division, NHSiS (1981) *Scottish Health Statistics 1979.*

9   Information and Statistics Division, NHSiS, *Scottish Health Statistics 1999.*

10 McGrother et al ibid.

11 *Grampian Strategy for People with Learning Disabilities,* 1997.

12 Scottish Office Health Department *Performance Monitoring Template 1997-98* Scottish Office.

13 Scottish Office Development Department *Local Financial Return (LFR 3) 1997/98* Scottish Office.

14 Information and Statistics Division NHSiS, *Scottish Health Statistics 1999,* ibid.

15 Scottish Office Health Department, (1994) *Community Care Bulletin.*

16 Scottish Executive *Community Care Statistics – Residential Care Information Note*, 1998.

17 Department of Health *Common Information Core 1997/98*.

18 Department of Health Statistical Bulletin *Personal Social Services – Current Expenditure in England 1997/98*.

19 National Assembly for Wales.

20 Scottish Office Health Department *Performance Monitoring Template*, ibid.

21 Scottish Office Development Department *(LFR 3)* ibid.

22 Ibid.

23 Information and Statistics Division (1999) *Scottish Health Services Costs 1998/99*.

24 The National Health Service and Community Care Act (1990).

25 The Scottish Office (1998) *Modernising Community Care –An Action Plan* HMSO.

26 Scottish Executive (1999) *Implementing Inclusiveness: Realising Potential – The Beattie Committee Report*, Scottish Executive.

27 Information and Statistics Division, NHSiS, *Scottish Health Statistics 1999*, ibid.

28 Scottish Office Health Department *Community Care Bulletin, 1997*.

29 Direct Payments Act (1996).

30 Jordan, R and Jones, G (1997) *Educational Provision for Children with Autism in Scotland*, University of Birmingham.

31 Mansell, J (1993) *Services for people with learning disability and challenging behaviour and mental health needs: Report of a Project Group*, London: HMSO.

32 Scottish Executive (1999) *The Riddell Advisory Committee Report on Education Provision for Children with Severe or Low Incidence Disabilities*, Scottish Executive.

33 Scottish Executive (1999) *If you don't ask you don't get! Learning Disability Review User and Carers Survey*, Scottish Executive.

34 Scottish Executive (1999) *The Beattie Committee Report*, ibid.

35 Scottish Health Advisory Service and The Scottish Office (1998) *Advocacy: A Guide to Good Practice*, The Scottish Office.

36 Scottish Human Services and Lanarkshire Health Board (draft December 1999) *Independent Advocacy. A guide for commissioners.*

37 Information and Statistics Division NHSiS, *Scottish Health Statistics 1999*, ibid.

38 ibid.

39 Scottish Executive *Community Care Statistics – Residential Care Information Note*, ibid.

40 Scottish Homes (1999) *Scotspen Annual Digest.*

41 Scottish Executive Health Department *Performance Management Template 1999/00.*

42 Ibid.

43 Scottish Executive (1999) *Housing Solutions*, Scottish Executive.

44 Scottish Executive (1999) *The View from Arthur's Seat*, Scottish Executive.

45 The Hester Adrian Research Centre for the Department of Health (1999) *The Quality and Cost of Residential Supports for People with Learning Disability*, Department of Health.

46 Costs for housing for small group homes and supported living, after an allowance of 40% for private finance, would cost £6.3 million over the three year period (in other words 330 x £19,200).

47 Scottish Executive Health Department *Community Care Statistics – Residential Care Information*, ibid.

48 Scottish Office Development Department *Local Financial Return*, ibid.

49 Scottish Office Health Department *Community Care Bulletin*, ibid.

50 Information and Statistics Division, NHSiS *Scottish Health Statistics 1999*, ibid.

51 Information and Statistics Division *Scottish Health Services Costs 1998/99*, ibid.

52 Department of Health (1999) *Facing the Facts: Services for People with Learning Disabilities*, HMSO.

53 Scottish Executive Health Department *Community Care Statistics*, unpublished data, 1998.

54 Scottish Office Development Department *Local Financial Return (LFR 3) 1997/98* unpublished.

55 Corbett, J ibid.

56 Scottish Executive *The View from Arthur's Seat*, ibid.

57 Stalker, K (ed.) (1996) *Developments in short-term care: Breaks and Opportunities*, London: Jessica Kingsley.

58 Lindsay, M, Kohls, M and Collins, J (1993) *The Patchwork Quilt: a study of respite services in Scotland*, Social Work Services Inspectorate.

59 Scottish Office Education Department (1998) *Education Statistics Division Schools Census*, Scottish Executive.

60 The Accounts Commission *Performance Information for Scottish Councils 1997/98*.

61 Lindsay et al ibid.

62 Scottish Office (1998) *Information Statistics Division Bulletin*.

63 Scottish Executive (1999) *Changing Public Attitudes to People with Learning Disabilities In Scotland*, Scottish Executive.

64 Enable (1999) *Stop it! Bullying and Harassment of People with Learning Disabilities*, Enable.

65 Sosbey, D, Gray, S and Wells D (1991) *Disability and Abuse: An Annotated Bibliography*, Baltimore: Paul H. Brooks.

66 Williams, C (1996) *Invisible Victims: Crime and Abuse about people with a learning disability*, London: Jessica Kingsley.

67 Mental Welfare Commission for Scotland (1998-9) *Annual Report*, Mental Welfare Commission.

68 Espie, C et al (1999) *The role of the NHS in meeting the health needs of people with learning disabilities*, Report for the Scottish Executive Learning Disability Review.

69 Beange H et al, ibid.

70 Hirst, N A (1985) 'Dependency and family care of young adults with disabilities', *Child care, Health and Development*, Volume 11 241-257.

71 Scottish Executive (1999) *Protecting the Vulnerable: Caring Enough? Guidance for Nurses, Midwives and Health Visitors.*

72 Hornby, G (1999) Inclusion or delusion: Can one size fit all? *Support and Learning: British Journal of Learning Support*, 14, 152-157.

73 The Scottish Executive (1999) *Helping Hands – Guidelines for staff who provide Intimate Care for Children and Young People with Disabilities.*

74 Scottish Executive (1999) *The Riddell Advisory Committee Report* ibid.

75 Mental Health Act 1984 *Section 106.*

76 Tymchuk, A J ' Predicting adequacy of parenting of people with mental retardation' *Child Abuse and Neglect*, Volume 16 165-178.

77 Hogg, J, Lucchino, R, Wang, K, Janicki, M (expected date of publication January 2000) *Health Ageing-Adults with Intellectual Disabilities Ageing and Social Policy A Report of the Ageing Special Interest Research Group of the International Association of the Scientific Study of Intellectual Disabilities*, WHO.

78 Ibid.

79 McGrother, C et al ibid.

80 Strauss, D, Sharvelle, R, Baumeister, A and Anderson, T W (1998) 'Mortality in persons with developmental disabilities after transfer to community care', *American Journal on Mental Retardation*, Vol 102 569-581.

81 Dodd, K, Brunler, J (1999) *Feeling Poorly – a package to enable people with learning disabilities to develop skills to communicate effectively about pain and illness*, Pavilion.

82 Millan Committee (1999) *First Consultation Paper April 1999.*

83 Russell, J and Roberston P *Use of Scottish Mental Health legislation in 1999 for people with learning disabilities*, Report to the Scottish Executive Learning Disability Review.

84 Cullen, C, Brown, F, Combes, H, Hendy, S (1999) 'Working with people who have intellectual impairments' in *What is Clinical Psychology?* Marzillier, J. and Hall, J (eds.) Oxford: Oxford University Press.

85 Mansell, J ibid.

86 Waitman, A, Corday-Hills, S (eds.) (1992) *Psychotherapy and Mental Handicap*, London, Sage.

87 Kroese, B, Dagnan, D, Loumidis, K (eds) (1997) *Cognitive Behaviour Therapy for People with Learning Disabilities*, London, Routledge.

88 O'Reilly, M (1997) 'Assessing challenging behaviour of persons with severe mental disabilities' in *Advances in Behaviour Analysis* Dillon Burger, K, O'Reilly, M and Keenan, M Dublin, Dublin University College.

89 Chadwick, O, Taylor, E and Benhard, S (1998) *The prevention of behaviour disorders in children with severe learning disability,* Report to NHS Executive London: Institute of Psychiatry.

90 Mental Welfare Commission for Scotland (1997) *Guidance on the Use of Restraint*, Mental Welfare Commission.

91 Reed, J *Review of Health and Social Services for Mentally Disordered Offenders and others requiring similar services: Report of the Political working Group on Services for People with Learning Disabilities.*

92 Lyall, I, Holland, A and Styles, P (1996) 'Incidents of Persons with a Learning Disability detained in Police Custody', *Journal of Intellectual Disability Research.*

93 Lyndsey, B et al (1998) 'Treatment of six men with a learning disability convicted of sex offences against children' *British Journal of Clinical Psychiatry, 37, 83-98.*

94 The Scottish Office (1999) *Health, Social Work and related Services for Mentally Disordered Offenders in Scotland*, The Scottish Office.

95 Scottish Executive (1999) *Making the Right Moves.*

96 Scottish Executive (1999) *The Riddell Advisory Committee Report*, ibid.

97 Scottish Executive (1999) *The Beattie Committee Report*, ibid.

98 Mental Health Foundation (1993) *Learning Disabilities: The Fundamental Facts*, London: Mental Health Foundation.

Designed and produced on behalf of the Scottish Executive by Tactica Solutions B12153 5/2000